LIVING WITH 2020 VISION

LIVING WITH 2020 VISION

THE MENTAL HEALTH AWAKENING IN THE BLACK COMMUNITY

TIARA JOHNSON

Bria,

Thanks for the support!

Tiara Johnson

NEW DEGREE PRESS

LIVING WITH 2020 VISION
The Mental Health Awakening in the Black Community

ISBN   978-1-63730-450-1   *Paperback*
          978-1-63730-557-7   *Kindle Ebook*
          978-1-63730-558-4   *Ebook*

To Mom and Miles,

I would like to thank you both for dealing with me and the ups and downs of my mental health journey over the years. Thank you for providing a safe space for me to explore my relationship with my mental wellness. I'll never forget when I decided to write this book, and you guys were my biggest supporters. There were times when the tears and stress of this author journey felt overwhelming, but you guys knew exactly what to say to ground me. I can't thank you enough for constantly believing in me, even in the moments when I doubted myself. I love you both so much!

PS: Sarah, a.k.a. "Mama," I know you are looking down on me and the family. I can only hope that this book and my achievement as an author and advocate has made you proud!

To my girlies,

I also want to thank my girlies Liv, Tyler, and Bri for being such a great support system for me. You guys never hesitated to listen to my long-winded rants and continued to check in on me even throughout my distant moments. When times were rough, I could always count on you guys to provide me with genuine love, laughter, and a listening ear. Thank you being a part of this journey with me. Love you guys forever!

Truly,
Teej

Contents

———

Introduction

——

"Everyone has their own personal pain and their own demons, and no one will talk about it, and that's why they never get better. They're all afraid to talk about it."
—TIFFANY HADDISH, THE LAST BLACK UNICORN

"Mental health" and the "Black community" are two terms that are rarely seen happily together. Most of the time, if the two terms are seen together, there seems to be an estranged relationship or alarming statistics following behind. It's far from a normalized relationship. Even though other communities have seemingly made the union look easy, it can still be an awkward or uncomfortable bond for the Black community for various reasons.

I like to compare it to dating. While other communities may find joy or ease in going on dates and getting to know others, members of the Black community may come with baggage, trauma, or trust issues from the past that make us more guarded or prone to managing difficulties alone. But does that mean we are undeserving of love or a chance at a healthy relationship? Are we, as a community, less deserving just because it may take us a little longer to get comfortable enough to share and showcase our vulnerability? Does this mean that we deserved to be left alone or ignored? When do we get the chance to be authentically seen, heard and understood for our experiences? When do we decide we need to be a part of the conversation?

Well, here's a spoiler alert. The chance is now. As a community, we are more than deserving of the opportunity to build a healthy relationship with mental health. I understand that we have been forced to normalize and overcome every adversity that has been thrown our way, regardless of its long-term effects. I understand that four hundred years of systematic oppression have resulted in generations of unhealed trauma that have not been taken seriously, until recently. After the painful events of 2020, certain themes like trauma, death and anxiety reached a breaking point and needed to be addressed by the community. As a collective, we were awakened and forced to address these themes with or without professional help from the mental health industry.

Luckily, I am not alone in my advocacy for mental health awareness and education in the African American community. The year 2020 even awakened public figures like actress Taraji P. Henson and Jada Pinkett-Smith to do their part to destigmatize mental health in our communities. Both women successfully merged their influence and status with social media platforms like Facebook to provide needed conversations surrounding mental health. As a Black woman, I am more than grateful for their representation. Both shows, *Red Table Talk* with Jada and *Peace of Mind with Taraji*, fill a necessary void within the Black community, by offering a safe space to normalize certain mental health stigmas.

As a self-proclaimed mental health advocate living in such a divisive and judgmental era, I also find myself idolizing those who aren't afraid to live unapologetically in their mental health truth. Coming from a community that normalizes pain, I realize how much courage it takes to live honestly in your mental health. Although mental health stigmas largely thrive in African American communities, both Tiffany Haddish and Charlamagne Tha God are among some of the very few celebrities that have never seemed hesitant to speak or shed light on their mental wellness journey. Instead, both influencers leveraged their personal experiences and became *New York Times* bestsellers by blending transparency with excellent storytelling skills.

I will never forget reading Charlamagne Tha God's first book in 2017, *Black Privilege.* It was one of the first times that I had ever heard someone in the Black community attempt to normalize therapy and mental health. It was refreshing to hear a different, more comforting, and relaxed tone surrounding depression and anxiety. Topics that at one point in time used to bring people shame. His next book, *My Anxiety Is Playing Tricks on Me,* was also successful, becoming a household name in the Black community and the mental health community. The book discussed his journey with fear and anxiety and how he has used that path to propel him to success. I think subconsciously, his book truly sparked my initial interest in the potential benefits of mental health education. He used relatable personal stories to not only entertain the audience, but also to educate the Black community on what anxiety, depression and trauma looks like, while sharing his experience with therapy. Ultimately, he made the topic of therapy seem like it was a life-changing event that I didn't need to miss out on.

In contrast with Tiffany Haddish's 2017 book, *The Last Black Unicorn*, she used her upsetting yet genuine life experiences to unveil a layer of intimacy that won over the hearts of her readers. As I read every intimate detail and story, I could immediately relate to the honesty and authenticity that was poured on the pages. Not every story or experience she faced was perfect or even positive, but throughout her storytelling, she successfully portrayed a new reality: one with a sense of clarity, peace and mental freedom that I aspired to achieve.

Let me be candid. Since 2018, I had been dealing with confusion surrounding my mental health journey, but I never decided to seek out mental health resources. Yes, I've experienced many mental health themes like death, depression, anxiety and trauma in my 25 years of life, which you'll learn more about later in the book. But, for some reason, I never felt the need or urgency to go seek therapy or a mental health professional. Like many members of the Black community, maybe I was conditioned to normalize traumatic experiences. Maybe subconsciously I was scared to unpack or address certain memories. It is hard to pinpoint where the initial hesitation came from, but all I can say is.... that changed in 2020.

Do you realize before even reading this book, we were all living with some form of 2020 vision? By that I mean, 2020 vision was how we remembered 2020 and its impact on us.

The Black community's attempts to undo four hundred years of systematic oppression were hindered severely by the countless rapid-fire tragedies during the pandemic that rocked many Black Americans to the core. To make a long and sad story short, the Black community experienced a triple pandemic. As a community, we were disproportionately affected health-wise, with COVID-19 deaths, and economically, with the loss of jobs and housing during the pandemic. Most importantly, we were disproportionately affected racially, from cops, "Karens" and "MAGA" supporters. We were forced into global isolation because of the pandemic. Then, we were forced to sit and watch countless Black men and women succumb to violence at the hands of police. We were also forced to grieve sudden deaths of celebrities and influencers in the community like Kobe Bryant, Chadwick Boseman, and Congressman John Lewis, while somehow finding the strength to support Black Lives Matter (BLM) protests for Breonna Taylor, George Floyd and many others. These painful events undoubtedly altered the mental wellbeing of the Black community as a whole.

Much like Tiffany Haddish's traumatic experiences forced her to embrace mental health as a "new reality," the compounded and traumatic events of 2020 awakened the Black community to this same "new reality" that most had been attempting to suppress over the years. I'll be the first to admit that until 2020, I had ignored the urges to seek therapy. I constantly made excuses and fell victim to the harmful stigmas. After surviving the chaos of 2020, I wondered if Tiffany's experience was unique. Does the number of traumatic events or type of trauma that you endure have any effect on how you approach seeking out mental health resources? Well, not to spoil it, but what I learned has changed the way I see our community dealing with mental health over the next decade.

With the compounding events of 2020 in consideration, it was evident that the need for mental health resources grew that year as well. According to research from Mental Health America (MHA), major depression is one of the most common mental illnesses, affecting 6.7 percent (more than 16 million) of American adults each year (Basic Facts About Depression, 2020). However, since the beginning of March 2020, MHA reported over 8 in 10 people who took a depression screening scored with symptoms of moderate to severe depression (Basic Facts About Depression, 2020).

The Anxiety and Depression Association of America reported that anxiety disorders are one of the more common mental illnesses in the US, affecting forty million adults in the United States aged eighteen and older, or 18.1 percent of the population every year (Facts and Statistics, 2020). In September 2020, MHA reported the rate of moderate to severe anxiety peaked, with over 8 in 10 people who took an anxiety screening scored with similar moderate to severe symptoms (A Growing Crisis, 2020).

However, members of the Black community have a different experience and understanding of anxiety and depression. In 2020, the American Psychological Association reported more than 2 in 5 (44 percent) African Americans state discrimination as a significant source of stress in their life, compared with 38 percent of people of color who said the same in 2019 (Stress in America, 2020). When it comes to the mental health of the Black community, there have always been some noticeable mental health service disparities. According to a Columbia University research study, although the Black community roughly constitute 12 percent of the United States population, they are overrepresented in high-risk populations (a group that is often impacted by specific negative occurrences) (Vance, 2019). For example, members of the Black community comprise approximately 40 percent of the homeless population, 50 percent of the prison population, and 45 percent of children in the foster care system (Vance, 2019). The same study also mentions that the Black community was disadvantaged in mental health through subjection to trauma through enslavement, oppression, colonialism, racism, and segregation. As a community we continue to feel the implications of these disadvantages.

Even before 2020, the African American community has found itself having a more difficult time being provided proper access to healthcare, education, and other fundamental resources. These disparities are not new and have even grown since the disproportionate economic and health impacts of 2020 occurred. According to a report from the National Institute of Health, racial and ethnic minorities that have less access to mental health services than Whites, are less likely to receive needed care and are more likely to receive poor quality care when treated. After entering care, minority patients are less likely than Whites to receive the best available treatments for depression and anxiety (McGuire & Miranda, 2014).

How are we supposed to face or obtain our new mental health reality, like Tiffany, when we are constantly struggling to retain access to resources and representation? As a community, how do we get the support and resources that we deserve? When will mental health resources be made more accessible for minority communities?

2020 holds a special place in all our lives, but the effects have been undoubtedly compounded for the Black community. Everyone seems to believe that despite four hundred years of systematic oppression and the recent triggering events of 2020, that the Black community is properly equipped with enough education and tools to combat everyday mental health struggles. However, I believe something else. I believe that 2020 can be seen as a mental health awakening in the Black community. I believe various events of 2020, like the nationwide protest for racial justice and the death of prominent Black public figures like Kobe Bryant and Chadwick Boseman, have leveraged the emotions and traumas of the Black community, waking us up to how our mental health is impacting us. However, because of the lack of mental health education, and lack of effective mental health resources, 2020 has left the Black community mentally fractured with no effective strategy in place to fix it.

I believe that 2020 awakened the Black community to six reoccurring mental health themes: death, grief, trauma, isolation, anxiety, and coping. I felt compelled to write this book because as a member of the Black community, I have gone through my own struggles with mental health. Personally, 2020 mentally impacted me and forced me to acknowledge aspects of my mental health journey that I had once attempted to ignore. I truly felt like I experienced a triple pandemic in 2020. I decided to protest for the first time ever, in honor of George Floyd and Breonna Taylor. That's where I had my first panic attack.

One would think that a panic attack would be a negative thing. But for me, I went through a wave of many emotions. I not only felt overwhelmed by the number of people and chanting, but by the warm feeling of "togetherness." Ultimately, that protest was a life-changing experience that changed my perception of mental health in my community.

The events of 2020 represent a true pivot in terms of mental health in the Black community. Because of the isolation, we were forced to begin to acknowledge those uncomfortable feelings and find ways to manage them. Now that we are awakening more than we have ever been collectively, it is time to give the community proper tools and resources to foster an amazing relationship with mental health.

That starts with you. Whether you are an advocate, ally or member of the Black community, I hope you walk away looking at the Black experience through a new lens: a more empathetic lens, with a better understanding of the often silenced and unhealed trauma of the Black community.

I hope that mental health professionals, local community leaders, and young progressives can also leverage their own emotions to be more empathetic to Black experiences while using their knowledge and resources to begin to lessen the gaps throughout mental health services and provide more accessible mental health education. But, if you can only walk away with one thing, walk away understanding that the events of 2020 have left the Black community to live and manage a new and uncomfortable reality: a reality that can only begin to adjust with encouragement and empathy from others.

CHAPTER 1

Science Behind Empathy and Comfort

———

"I've learned that people will forget what you said, people will forget what you did, but people will never forget how you made them feel."

—*MAYA ANGELOU*

When I looked up the definition of the word "empathy" online, *Merriam-Webster Dictionary* defined it as the action of understanding, being aware of, being sensitive to, and vicariously experiencing the feelings, thoughts, and experience of another of either the past or present.

Long before I had ever heard or learned of the idea of empathy, it was evident to me that I rarely struggled with showing empathy or being able to "put myself in someone else's shoes," as my mom would call it. Luckily, empathy seemed to be one trait that came naturally to me.

As a child growing up, I knew how it felt when it seemed like my opinions were being disregarded, not acknowledged or fully understood. I remember the feeling of complete discouragement. I remember being frustrated when I would attempt to explain my views on everyday topics like favorite songs or favorite subjects in school. In those moments, instead of responding as though my standpoints were heard, they were never acknowledged and were oftentimes ignored. For a while, I considered there was something wrong with my answers or ideas.

So, I tried a different route. Instead of solely giving out my opinions, I began to ask others first, to see if I could find similarities. I quickly learned that when I began responses with similarities from others, my opinions that followed were better received. I told myself, in order to stop the feelings of discouragement and hurt, maybe it would be best for me to begin to learn about others, namely their experiences and thought process. The way I looked at it, if I could understand their experiences, then I could better understand how they communicate, and ultimately, I could communicate more effectively with others. In return, I hoped that they would become more receptive to my feelings, fostering a better understanding and potential relationship.

Since then, I have continued to intentionally practice empathy with others because I see how rewarding it can be. To feel heard by someone is priceless. Over the years, I realized the connection between communication and empathy. If you know how to effectively talk to others, you can better empathize and comfort them as well.

In high school, I found a love and talent for writing. What started as an initial interest in writing quickly blossomed to a passion for storytelling, and I went on to graduate with a BA in Journalism. But I wanted to learn more. I decided it would be best to spend the next few years gaining more understanding and education in the power of communications, and more specifically, strategic communications. While earning my Master of Professional Studies (MPS) in Public Relations and Corporate Communications from Georgetown University, I learned that the true power of strategic communications is the ability to use intentional or tactical wording to satisfy the goals of the client.

I have spent my last few educational years experimenting with my personal blend of communications and empathy and how it can best serve others. Ultimately, I have found that communication and empathy can be used to provide comfort to others. I found that when you have empathy toward someone's experiences, there is a better long-term chance for creating more meaningful conversations and relationships.

It is paramount for readers to understand the importance of empathy, so that they can create more impactful and comforting conversations about mental health and its relationship, particularly in the Black community. Now, that being said, if I am expecting you guys to walk away viewing the Black experience through a more empathetic lens, I figured it would be beneficial to address the science behind empathy. So, I went on a search to learn more about the science behind empathy and was pleased to know that I was on the right track when it comes to looking at empathy as a solution to providing comfort to others in their time of need.

According to a 2020 *Psychology Today* online article, empathy is a one-on-one connection because of a deep understanding that comes from sharing an emotional experience. Sympathy is a feeling of sadness or pity felt for another person (Davis, 2020). The main difference between the two terms is how they can make the one who suffers feel. The Black community has never asked for or wanted sympathy or pity from others. We only want empathy and understanding from others.

Sympathy doesn't require much self-reflection and can sound like "I'm so sorry to hear that," or "I feel bad for you." Whereas empathy requires you to actively listen and then reflect internally before responding with follow up questions. Oftentimes empathy is less verbal, more present and can sound like "I can only imagine how you felt in that moment," or "How are you handling it today?" When you intentionally show empathy, you find yourself asking more questions to learn more about the feelings of that person, rather than solely responding with additional statements.

SCIENCE BEHIND EMPATHY AND COMFORT

When I began my initial search for the science behind empathy, I ran across a 2017 *NIH (National Institute of Health)* online published journal titled, "The Science of Empathy." It looked at therapists, counselors, and psychologists as health care workers. The publication discussed the importance of having empathy as a personal trait and proved with its presented research that using empathy among health care providers had a direct correlation to patient satisfaction and trust.

Empathy also requires cognitive, emotional, behavioral, and moral capacities to understand and respond to the suffering of others (Riess. 2017). Looking further into this 2017 journal, empathy plays a critical interpersonal and societal role, enabling sharing of experiences, needs, and desires between individuals and providing an emotional bridge that promotes prosocial behavior (Riess 2017). Having and effectively using empathy can help build an emotional connection that can promote social behaviors like helping and sharing, which can benefit other people or society as a whole.

In addition to those prosocial behaviors, I firmly believe that empathy promotes basic humanity and decency among others. This means that as decent human beings on Earth, we never want to feel judged. Ideally, we as humans just want to be treated fair and equally. Oftentimes, in order to feel equal, there needs to be empathy present to show the similarities. The publication mentioned the science, this capacity of empathy requires an exquisite interplay of neural networks and enables us to perceive the emotions of others, resonate with them emotionally and cognitively, to take in the perspective of others, and to distinguish between our own and others' emotions (Riess, 2017).

As I continued to read more details about the neuroscience behind empathy, I began to get discouraged because it initially seemed that there was a chance that empathy could not be taught. I mean, whether a person can be taught virtue is a valid debate. But then, the same 2017 *NIH* publication mentioned that in the past, empathy was considered an inborn trait which could not be taught, but research has shown that this vital human competency is mutable and can be taught to health-care providers (Riess, 2017). Now, if it could be taught to health care providers, then what was stopping others in the world from learning about the benefits of empathy?

What is the difference between empathetic health care providers and empathetic American citizens? Both groups have the potential of daily interaction with others from different cultures and backgrounds, right? However, I feel there is a difference. Compared to the average health care providers, the average citizen is not professionally encouraged to be empathetic. But the average American can, or should be motivated to be empathetic. This is why empathy can be one of the many plausible solutions to help bridge the gaps between the Black community and the mental health industry.

But how does one actively begin to practice empathy? Well, according to the *NIH* publication, it starts with self-empathy. Self-empathy is as straightforward as it sounds. It means to show or have empathy with oneself. According to the *NIH* publication, human beings have intricate, shared neural circuits in motor, sensory, and emotional (limbic) areas of the brain to help them understand the experience of others, leading to helping behaviors (Riess. 2017). However, when emotionally overloaded, overwhelmed, exploited, or burned out, the capacity for empathy declines as a result of the degree of emotional labor expended (Riess. 2017). So, in order to maintain healthy levels of empathy, one must regularly exercise self-care and empathy first.

The publication concluded its findings and mentioned that self-empathy and other empathy lead to replenishment and renewal of a vital human capacity, and that the cardinal feature of empathy is that it usually helps connect people to others (Riess. 2017). Even though ideally, it seems easier to connect with people with whom you share similarities, there are benefits to intentionally showing empathy to individuals with different backgrounds. The *NIH* publication stated, cognitive empathy must play a role when a lack of emotional empathy exists because of racial, ethnic, religious, or physical differences (Riess. 2017).

Realistically, I think one of the many solutions lies at the intersection of empathy and comfort. The term "comfort" is defined by the *Oxford English Dictionary* as the easing or alleviation of a person's feelings of grief or distress. But when you think about it, how do you provide others with comfort? Do you know what to say to others when you see them upset?

Jen Marr, author and Founder and CEO of Inspiring Comfort, a company dedicated to teaching comfort as a skill, explains that 75 percent of people feel that they can recognize someone who is struggling but only 15 percent of people feel equipped to know what to say or do to support them (Inspiring Comfort, n.d). This is what is known as the "empathy-action gap." Jen Marr and her organization have been working as pioneers in establishing comfort as a teachable skill.

Marr discussed her research on the PAUSE method and its benefits to helping lessen the empathy-action gap with me. According to Jen, the PAUSE technique or filter can be used when you are attempting to figure out how to best comfort someone. Before you open your mouth to respond and help someone, ask yourself am I "present" with the person? Am

I exhaling and being there in the moment for that person? Next, "advice." We tend to want to offer advice first, but that often isn't comforting because nobody deals with issues in the same way. So "A" actually stands for not giving advice unless specifically asked. Then we have "unloading." Before responding or unloading your own thoughts on how you would handle the given situation, ask yourself, "does misery really love company?" You may want to let the other person know that you have gone through similar experiences but refrain from unloading yourself on the other person.

Next, "stay." When someone is going through a tragedy, you may want to cheer them up. You are attempting to move them out of their current mood. But in reality, to truly provide care and comfort, you want to stay with their mood. Lastly, "emphasis." Is the emphasis on you or the other person? A lot of the time, we end up putting the emphasis on ourselves instead of the one that is suffering, because it's more familiar to talk about ourselves rather than someone else. But it is important to keep the emphasis on that person, so they know you care.

Even before 2020, face-to-face connectivity was on the decline. Now, given the long-term impacts of quarantine and isolation, there is greater need for human care and connection. When I talked with Jen Marr, she explained that everyone has their own comfort styles, but the process starts by seeing those around us who are hurting, identifying appropriate action, intentionally connecting, and reflecting on how it helped us and determining what more can be done.

She helped me realize that comfort is more than a noun. It's also a powerful, resilient verb. Based on its Latin origins, "com" means together with, and "fort" means "strength". This means that through comfort, you can provide others with strength to handle adversity and trauma.

You may be surprised to find out the similarities you share with someone when you intentionally practice empathy.

Empathy and comfort are both tools that can be used to show others that they matter. Even simply taking time out of your day to sit still and actively listen to the feelings of others can be extremely productive for both parties. Oftentimes, people feel like they don't have the right words in the moment to support a person. However, remember the PAUSE technique because true comfort exists when you truly feel heard.

CHAPTER 2

2020 Triple Pandemic

Not everything that is faced can be changed. But nothing can be changed until it is faced.

—*JAMES BALDWIN*

I was causally headed to the kitchen when I walked past the TV, which had the news playing in the background, and I heard the term "triple pandemic" for the first time.

It was another Monday in lockdown. Up until this point, I knew that the pandemic was affecting me in more ways than one, but I hadn't found the right words to articulate my feelings. Then, I heard the term "triple pandemic" and I immediately found comfort. The term immediately reconfirmed all the trauma that I experienced over the last eight months.

I was fixing lunch when I heard the phrase that summed up what I'd been thinking: triple pandemic. I turned the stove off, went to the living room, and sat to hear the rest of the news report. It wasn't until November 2020 when someone finally described what we'd been experiencing.

Like most, I had never actively lived through a pandemic and was only partially familiar with the 1918 influenza pandemic. But frankly, I was just not prepared for all the lasting emotions, feelings, and trauma that came along with surviving a pandemic. The "triple pandemic" for the Black community refers to three different sectors of the Black experience that have disproportionately been impacted as a result of events in 2020. For the Black community, 2020 disproportionately affected us from a health, economic and racial perspective.

HEALTH

From a health perspective, the entire country was impacted by the global pandemic and its alarming number of COVID-19 related deaths. According to the Center for Disease Control (CDC) Data Tracker, there had been 22 million reported Covid cases and over 300,000 reported Covid deaths in the US as of December 2020. However, people with certain underlying health conditions like diabetes and heart conditions were at greater risk of being infected.

From a systematic standpoint, a *Reuters* report entitled "The Race Gap," explains that the life expectancy gap between Black (72.2) and white (76.6) people has remained at four years while chronic diseases, such as heart conditions or cancer, continue to strike Black people at higher rates than white people.

Additionally, the report continues to state that health insurance, a solid indicator of healthcare access, has eluded Black adults more than it has eluded White adults for a multitude of reasons. The gap in coverage between White and Black adults has been almost cut in half after the 2010 passage of the Affordable Care Act, from 9.9 percentage points to 5.5 in 2016, explained the study. But progress has since stalled. The remaining gap may be a factor of lower incomes, or the type of jobs Black people are more likely to hold. But the disparity in coverage means Black people are more likely to avoid care due to cost (Hartman & Hart, 2021).

Because of systematic oppression and lack of access to proper resources, the Black community was immediately impacted by COVID-19 related deaths. According to the *National Institute of Health* article, as of August 18, 2020, the national COVID-19 mortality rate for Black Americans was 2.1 times higher than that of Whites. Although Blacks make up 13 percent of the US population, over 30 percent had been diagnosed with COVID-19 infections (Laurencin & Walker, 2020).

If you ask a member of the Black community if they have been either directly or indirectly affected by a COVID-19 related death, nine times out of ten, they will have been impacted more than once.

ECONOMIC

From an economic perspective, because of the global pandemic and immediate quarantine, the Black community was once again disproportionately impacted. The economy took an immediate fall, which most called the worst recession since 2008. In the Black community, the unemployment fears loomed in the back of the mind of most. Some people were forced to make difficult decisions when it came to figuring out how to survive during economic distress and uncertainty.

The economic hardships were compounding for the Black community because even before 2020, we were struggling for economic freedom, in terms of living comfortably and acquiring generational wealth. Black Americans have one tenth net worth ($18k) of white Americans ($171k) (Hartman & Hart, 2021). Nearly one in five Black households has net worth of zero or less than zero dollars, compared to the same being true for nearly one in ten White households (Hartman & Hart, 2021)). So, as a community, we have been systematically fighting for years to be offered the same access to wealth (Hartman & Hart, 2021).

The *Reuters* report confirms that before the 2008 housing crisis, Black consumers were disproportionately targeted for predatory loans, making them more vulnerable to foreclosures. And Black people buying homes today often pay higher mortgage fees and face more setbacks from tighter underwriting standards, according to the study. Those who can buy homes often get fewer financial benefits because properties in predominately Black neighborhoods appreciate more slowly than those in predominately White areas, contributing to broader gaps in family wealth, according to the *Reuters* study.

So in 2020, it was no surprise that some members of the Black community found themselves struggling financially while also being laid off from work during the COVID-19 pandemic. According to *Statista* report, in 2020, the national unemployment rate stood at 8.1 percent. At the same time, 11.7 percent of the Black or African American population in the United States was unemployed, marking the highest unemployment rate of any ethnicity, explained the *Statista* report.

Others like front-line workers in the grocery stores and food services found themselves as "essential workers," forced to work in high-risk environments. According to an *Economic Policy Institute* article, Black workers make up about one in six of all front-line-industry workers (Gould & Wilson. 2020). These same individuals had to put themselves at great personal risk for minimum wage and often aren't even making enough livable wage.

One of United States' solutions to the economic crisis in 2020 was providing Paycheck Protection Program (PPP) loans to small businesses. But once again, qualifying minority and Black-owned businesses didn't reap the full benefits. According to the National Institute of Economic Development, 2017 Census data showed that minority owned businesses made up 31 percent of employer and non-employer firms, while non-minority owned businesses made up 68 percent of total businesses in the US.

During the first period of PPP loan distribution, loan data in which respondents answered the demographic question on race showed that non-minority applicants received 83 percent of loans and minority businesses only received 17 percent (Venderbeek, 2021). The National Institute of Economic Development also stated that specific Black owned businesses only received 1.6 percent of loans when they made up 10 percent of US businesses owners according to US Census data.

No matter how you attempt to approach it, there is no denying that the Black community has been disproportionately affected economically.

RACIAL

Race was one of the more important themes of 2020. However, it's important to note that the strained relationship between the Black community, the police, and the justice system began many years ago. Since 2014, we have seen major incidents involving police officers killing Black men, like the police shootings of Eric Garner and Michael Brown. Black people also have a greater chance of dying from an encounter with a police officer, compared with White people (Hartman & Hart, 2021)

Based on the Reuters report about the race gap, Black Americans face a higher chance of imprisonment. In 2017, Black adults made up 33 percent of the U.S prison population despite accounting for only 12 percent of the nation's adult population. In contrast, White people made up 30 percent of the prison population but 64 percent of the country as a whole, according to the report. Additionally, a Sentencing Commission report examined the difference in federal court sentences found that between 2007 and 2016, sentences for Black male offenders were an average of almost 20 percent longer than those for White male offenders accused of the same crime (Hartman & Hart, 2021).

In 2020, the Black community witnessed and shared the frustration of having to watch viral videos of George Floyd, Breonna Taylor, and countless other African Americans being violently killed by police officers. According to a *Washington Post* article, Black Americans accounted for less than 13 percent of the US population in 2020, but were killed by police at more than twice the rate of White Americans (Washington Post, 2020). Another NBC News article explained that police in the US killed 164 Black people in the first 8 months of 2020 (Cohen, 2020). According to the website Mapping Police Violence, which tracks data on police violence in the country, police killed Black people at higher rates than White people in forty-seven of the fifty largest US cities (Mapping Police Violence, 2021). Ultimately, as a community, we decided to protest and wake the world up to our continued hurt and pain. But it seems like a lot of those efforts ultimately fell on deaf ears.

If that wasn't enough stress, the Trump administration spent the previous four years creating divisiveness toward minorities and Black communities in America. Over his presidential term, Trump created an excited a fan base that thrived off violence and racism.

Even the American Psychological Association's chief of psychology and acting chief of diversity Brian Smedley, noted in an NBC News article that "these compounding issues— ones that come with uncertainty and old traumas— have psychologists looking at a 'mental health tsunami' in the Black community," (Madani, 2020). The NBC News article continued to go into detail about how there are unmet needs for the Black community within the mental health space.

Brian Smedley continued to discuss the fact that "the combination of physical distancing, economic anxiety, and for people of color, the very real stress from the racism pandemic means that we will have a lot of unmet mental health needs unless we can dramatically shore up the mental health infrastructure and address workforce shortages," (Madani. 2020).

Similar to Smedley's explanation, I agree that the mental health infrastructure and workforce shortage needs to be addressed. I believe that that starts with basic mental health awareness and education within the Black community. This starts with getting the Black community to understand and begin to vocalize and identify the impact of triggers like racial trauma and anxiety that have been exposed during the triple pandemic.

Unlike the global pandemic that was experienced worldwide, the triple pandemic was unique to the Black community. From health, economic and racial perspectives, the Black community was disproportionately impacted. The compounded mental, emotional, and physical trauma and stress can have a lasting impact on the mental health of the Black community. I believe that the triple pandemic ultimately sparked a mental health awakening. Now it is time to begin to get comfortable having the conversations about the impact of systematic oppression in Black community and how it continues to affect our mental health.

CHAPTER 3

My Introduction to Mental Health

___

"The hardest part was finding the courage to give myself permission to do things differently."

—*TIARA JOHNSON*

It wouldn't be fair to ask others to trust me enough to tell their intimate stories of 2020 throughout this book without taking the time to be vulnerable and tell my story and journey first. Interestingly enough, my story begins in 2018.

For a long time, I thought if I tried to ignore certain themes in my life, or simply didn't speak about certain situations, somehow everything would work out with time. But that wasn't the case. I attempted to adopt this "push through and overcome" mentality, hoping to mask emotions that were too confusing to manage and sort through. Unfortunately, all my efforts were unsuccessful for me in the long-term.

I finally realized that the only thing that was changing was the date. Days would turn into weeks, weeks into months, and months into a year of constant, unfortunate news and unfamiliar emotions. It was evident to me that I was falling deeper into this downward spiral. By that point, I had wasted almost two years of my life avoiding feelings and issues within myself, only to find myself in a worse mental and physical state than the one I had when I began. So, I decided to finally do something different, and I'm glad I did.

You don't have to be great to get started. But you have to get started to be great.

—LES BROWN

Let me just tell you now: this is not a story about how my mental health was saved with one pleasant visit to the therapist. Actually, I still have yet to speak with or schedule an appointment with a therapist.

I do believe in the benefits of therapy and plan to seek out therapy or other mental health resources in the future. But I don't think that therapy is the only beneficial solution, especially when a large percentage of Black Americans, like me, are disproportionately affected by the lack of readily available mental health resources in lower socioeconomic communities. So, this is my story of how I addressed and attempted to manage my mental health journey, within my given situation.

I would label myself as your average, 25-year-old millennial, constantly trying to find my true purpose in the world. I grew up in a single-parent household on the eastside of Atlanta as the oldest sibling out of two, so I quickly found myself with a lot of responsibilities. But from a young age, I always had a strong desire to do what was needed to make my close-knit family proud. This is why, even to this day, I struggle with balancing my "free-spirit" millennial-self, with the "work first" Gen X mentality with which I was raised.

Throughout my life, my mother taught me that education and higher learning would be the key to my success. It was the way to break generational curses. I saw it as one of the only ways to potentially create a better life for myself, and for future generations. So, I focused my time and energy on making the best of my educational opportunities (because clearly I wasn't the athletic type). I went on to graduate *cum laude* from Georgia State University with a BA in Journalism, and a minor in Marketing, and then proceeded to obtain my MPS (Master of Professional Studies) in Public Relations and Corporate Communications from Georgetown University. I quickly found solace in being able to use higher education and more specifically, strategic communications, as a way to change and advance my current situation.

However, the journey to this point has not been easy. I realized that my first true introduction to my personal mental health struggles began in late 2018 early 2019, with what I initially labeled as my "quarter-life crisis."

I think most would agree that after graduating from undergraduate programs, most college students are excited to be moving into apartments and starting their first adult jobs, in an attempt to begin their professional career. Unfortunately for me, that was never my case. After graduating in May 2018 and for the next several months, I was constantly applying to jobs and hearing the phrase "we will be moving forward with other applicants." I found myself living back at home and falling into a deep "slump" or depression that I couldn't seem to shake. I just remember joking with close friends saying "I don't even know how to describe it. I just feel lost in life, unmotivated, and confused, almost like a mid-life crisis, but before I'm twenty-five."

The entire year of 2019 was filled with fighting or attempting to ignore my own personal mental health demons. For the first eight months of the year, I spent my days confined to my room, searching for jobs and sending in job applications, and often sleeping through disappointment and depression. I gained a lot of weight, ghosted a lot of close friends, and even lost motivation for higher education. I just wasn't myself, mentally, emotionally, and physically.

One day, many months into the depression, I remember my mother asked me "Why are you always just laying around? Why don't you get up and go do something?" I've grown used to her bluntness, but I think it comes from being raised in New York. Frankly, at that moment, she was also tired of coming home from her job every day and seeing me on the couch, doing nothing.

She may not have said the best thing she could have said in the situation, but she's not a trained therapist who understands clinical depression, or a perfect, ideal person who always knows what you need to hear. She's just my mom, and she was worried about me and scared that I was wasting my youth being idle.

"You can't tell? I don't want to do anything... I'M DEPRESSED!" I screamed in frustration.

I think I yelled at her, because subconsciously, I was yelling at myself too. All these months, I had been routinely asking myself that exact same question, without being able to vocalize my feelings and answer. But that was the first time I was able to communicate that I was in fact dealing with depression. Big first steps for me.

"Look, all you need to do is just stop lying around, get up, and make an effort to do something today. Have you applied to any jobs today?" my mother said in a similar blunt tone.

I'm not going to lie. Initially, I was baffled that it seemed as though nobody around me, even my closest family members, could see me suffering. Maybe I had been really good at putting on the right faces at the moment? But I knew that truthfully, I felt alone and vulnerable and being able to finally vocalize my feelings of depression felt freeing. At that moment, I really didn't know how I expected my mom to react. I think I wanted to hear "Don't worry. I know how to fix you. You don't have to suffer alone anymore." But I realized that was unrealistic. There is never a quick fix to mental health, but a constant journey. I can't and shouldn't assume that someone else has the magic tool to automatically fix me. I quickly learned that I had to want to fix myself, for myself.

In my mom's defense, when I look back on that moment, I am grateful that I was able to experience a moment of realization with her. I realized that I needed to have that conversation with her. I finally realized that she did notice some changes in my mood and behavior, which is why she attempted to communicate those feelings to the best of her ability. Honestly, I truly thank her for that moment because after that, I was on the path to finding myself again.

Having to say the words "depression," "anxiety," or even "mental health" is difficult because these words are oftentimes attached to many stigmas in the Black community. But since I didn't have anyone to help sort through my feelings, I was forced to sort through them on my own. I would say the process took about 6 months, and it wasn't easy.

I remember listening to the May 22, 2019 *Breakfast Club* interview with Humble the Poet, an educator and international best-selling author, who was there to promote his new book, *Unlearn*. If you haven't seen the interview or read the book, I highly suggest both.

By the end of the 25-minute interview, I felt like new life had been put into me. I felt like I had a purpose and newfound direction. Throughout the entire interview, host Charlamagne Tha God bragged about how the book, *Unlearn*, was filled with so many important pieces of life advice that could have an immediate effect on changing one's life for the better. Humble the Poet explained that ultimately, the purpose of the book was to let readers know that it is ok to unlearn certain things that you were taught growing up. Sometimes we learn things in, or for the moment, but it is okay to mature and unlearn those same attitudes in order to better your life.

Listening to that interview felt like someone was finally telling me it was okay to unlearn the expected or associated stigmas linked with mental health in the Black community. In that moment, I felt like I was hearing that it was okay to unlearn the "push through and overcome" and "showing emotions is a weakness" mentalities, along with so many other attitudes I was taught growing up.

It didn't take me long to order and read the entire book. It was a quick read, filled with over 90 two-page chapters with quotes and advice on how to unlearn certain themes in your life. Out of the whole book, there were two specific chapters or lessons that helped to shift my mentality and ultimately help support me though my new relationship with mental health.

I remember reading Chapter 12 of Unlearn, titled "When was the world ever fair?" I could immediately relate to the title because as an African American, I constantly feel like the world isn't fair and definitely is not equal for us. But I had normalized that idea and adapted a "the strong will survive" attitude. But according to Humble the Poet, "The strongest don't survive; the most adaptable do. When life is viewed this way, nothing is seen as an obstruction, but merely an obstacle to overcome" (Humble the Poet, pg 41). I decided to unlearn the need to rely on "being strong" in the face of adversity and instead learn how to be more adaptable. For me, that meant that I needed to learn more about mental health awareness and education so that when I was faced with another mental health obstacle, I would have the proper knowledge to better adapt to those new feelings.

When I read Chapter 98, "Don't Hold Yourself Back," I imme-diately realized that for the past almost two years (2018-2020),

I had been holding myself back. Instead of continuing to make the best of the situation I had been given, I chose to let my sadness and self-pity cripple me from achieving my full potential. Humble the Poet mentioned, "When we further carve and clarify our chosen purpose on this planet, we'll start to realize when we hit roadblocks that many of them are self-imposed. We give ourselves reasons not to take the leap and that is a sure sign that we're allowing our fears to get the best of us," (Humble the Poet, pg 293). I realized that I was hitting roadblocks in both my personal and professional life, because I had spent years ignoring feelings and delaying the needed work on myself.

Looking back on it, I believe I probably ignored those feelings of failure and unhappiness because it was easier to handle. I assumed if I didn't address or acknowledge those feelings then they would magically disappear one day. But that never happened. Instead, I had to make a conscious decision to address my sadness, no matter how much I was afraid of the unknown. I can't say that there was a specific day or event that made me decide to unlearn these habits. All I can say is, I remember waking up one day and saying to myself "I'm tired of being sad." I could remember cheerful times from my past, and I was truly desperate to try anything to experience that happiness again. So, I decided that from that day on, I would unlearn the ways in which I ignored my emotions, and I would begin to prioritize my mental health journey.

By January 2020, I believed that I had mastered the art of addressing depression and other mental health issues involved in a quarter-life crisis. I understood that in order to keep a positive mindset and manage my unhappiness, I had to realize that I needed to feel comfortable living with my feelings and learning to be more adaptable. I realized that life would be filled with both good and bad days and that it is important to not get stuck in a particular mindset.

So, 2020 started great for me. My mental health journey had been going well, and my educational motivation was back. I had worked hard and had just been accepted for a diversity fellowship at a global PR firm, beating out 30 other applicants. Because my initial mental health journey taught me to celebrate the small victories, I decided to take a spring break trip to Jamaica with a childhood friend. I had never been out of the country, and I was mentally exhausted and felt like I deserved this trip. It wasn't until I returned from my trip that 2020 took a monstrous turn.

The announcement of COVID-19, followed by a nationwide quarantine, affected me more than I expected. By the time I got home from the airport, the state of Georgia was in the process of being put under official lockdown. Schools were being shut down, grocery stores were being invaded for toilet tissue, and it was safe to say the country was in a bit of a panic.

Because I was no stranger to sitting still for months during my quarter-life crisis, the thought of quarantining was not intimidating. I quickly found myself coaching my family and others on strategies to best handle the mental stress of nationwide quarantine. "It's easier said than done, but you have to keep a routine going during these times and try not to get stuck thinking about the negatives," I told both my mother and brother.

But it wasn't until I received the dreaded phone call that I began to second-guess my own mental health strategies and progress.

"Hi, am I speaking with Miss Johnson?" the pleasant voice on the other end of the phone asked.

"Hi, yes. This is she. Who's calling?" I responded.

"I'm with Ketchum PR and I was calling to let you know that we were really looking forward to having you be a part of our Diversity Fellowship program this summer. But because of the uncertainty caused by COVID-19 and the new quarantine restrictions, we will not be able to offer this opportunity this year."

I was immediately at a loss for words, and I attempted to remain as professional as possible. To be honest, the call felt like a nightmare. Within 5 minutes, it seemed like my dreams were swiftly taken away.

I could feel the dark cloud of depression beginning to loom over me, but I was determined to not let those feelings consume my mind. The next day, I spent four hours on LinkedIn applying to any and every job that had the words "communications," "remote," or "paid" in the title.

Within a week, I had received a job as a remote test administrator for Pearson. Keep in mind, this was my first official job since I graduated from an undergraduate program over 18 months earlier. For the following four months, I worked as hard as ever to maintain this job. I was dedicated to showing my employers that I was effective at my job. For a moment, I had even forgotten I was still living through a pandemic. Working remotely allowed me to stay safe and quarantined while making money. Unfortunately, the happiness didn't last long... and neither did the job.

I was let go, again, due to the impact of COVID-19 on the economy. A CNN article discussed how 30 million Americans had filed for unemployment benefits since mid-March 2020 (Anneken, 2020). Talk about a gut punch, huh? After all that work and determination, it almost felt like I was back at square one, which was depressing.

According to the Mental Health America organization, adult Blacks and African Americans are more likely to have feelings of sadness, hopelessness, and worthlessness than adult Whites (Mental Health America, 2020). On top of that, the shooting and unfortunate death of Breonna Taylor had been replaying in my head and subconsciously affecting my mental health. I felt like I was about to mentally break down, and that thought scared me more than anything.

Despite the negative thoughts and constant obstacles in 2020, I continued to recite positive mindset mantras and quotes from Humble the Poet. I gave myself permission to feel my feelings, but not to get stuck. I changed my mindset to understand that life is filled with uncontrollable ups and downs.

In the last two months of 2020, through consistency and an adjusted mindset, I ended up accomplishing a lot of goals. Even though I was rejected by over thirty different employers since 2018, I ended up finding my educational purpose for corporate diversity and inclusion and realized my passion for mental health education and awareness. I was able to support my family during these uneasy moments of 2020. More importantly, I had the courage to keep going.

Like many people throughout the world, I encountered some trying and traumatic events during and prior to 2020. The hardest part of this journey has been finding the courage to give myself permission to do things differently. The process has had its uncomfortable moments, but I have been able to truly master the art of refocusing and shifting my mindset, which has proven beneficial to my mental wellbeing, and hopefully can serve others like mine, with a similar story.

Don't let the hard times define your experience. Oftentimes, in the midst of your lowest moments, your greater purpose can begin to blossom.

CHAPTER 4

Isolation and Education

———

When they are alone, they want to be with others, and when they are with others, they want to be alone. After all, human beings are like that.

—GERTRUDE STEIN

The majority of Americans did not expect the initial lockdown to last as long as it did. What started out for most as a two-week shelter-in-place mandate, gradually resulted in many states commanding residents to quarantine for months. This is where we saw the impacts of isolations begin.

Now, it may have been easy for some people for forgot just how much chaos erupted in the first few months of 2020. But others will forever remember just how hectic we were as a country, when we were introduced to the pandemic. According to a 2020 report from the Brookings Institution, a nonprofit public policy organization in Washington, DC, while mistakes were inevitable in the face of such a massive and rapidly evolving domestic and global challenge, it can be argued that there were massive failures of judgment and inaction in January, February, and even March of that year.

Based on the same Brookings Institution report, the following information details a condensed timeline of events that happen within the first three months of 2020:

January:
- From the first knowledge of the virus's spread in Wuhan in early January through nearly the end of that month, the US administration publicly treated the virus as a minor threat that was under control, at least domestically, and repeatedly assured the public that the risk to Americans was very low.
- On January 17, the CDC started screening passengers who had been traveling in Wuhan at three US airports, but by then the virus had already spread to countries other than China.
- On January 27, the White House created the Coronavirus Task Force (publicly announced on January 29) followed by the declaration of a public health emergency on January 31.
- By the end of the month, there were about 12,000 reported cases in China, growing rapidly by the day; at this point, the US had a handful of confirmed cases.

February:
- The CDC developed its own test in early February, which was then distributed to labs. But, as became clear roughly a week later, one of the reagents in its kits proved to be faulty, which meant that most labs were unable to proceed using CDC test kits.

- The CDC was reassuring state and local officials that testing capacity was adequate in late February, although it was reported that fewer than 500 tests had been conducted at that point. This took majority of the month.
- By the end of the month, the urgency began to shift. The CDC widening testing criteria on February 28 and the Food and Drug Administration began allowing the use of non-approved tests (with retroactive approval) on February 29.
- By the end of the month, the United States had two dozen confirmed cases (artificially low numbers because of the low levels of testing), China reportedly had about 80,000 cases.

March:
- On March 11, President Trump's nationally televised address, in tandem with his March 13 declaration of a national emergency, finally saw the federal government fully engage its efforts to hasten mass testing, improve the availability of medical supplies, and encourage all Americans to radically alter their behavior in order to arrest the spread of the virus.
- Commercial tests were approved quickly, and mass testing finally became a reality—which, in turn, helped reveal the considerably advanced spread of the virus in the US.
- Over the month of March, confirmed cases in the United States increased at a rapid clip, passing 100 (3/5), then 1,000 (3/11), then 10,000 (3/18), and by the end of the month 100,000 (3/27), reflecting in part that our testing capacity had begun to catch up with the reality on the ground.

It seemed as though almost immediately after Trump declared coronavirus as a national emergency in March, the American people went into a frenzy. There was a rush to the grocery stores, where we were met with long lines and fights over sanitizer and toilet paper. At the same time, there was an immediate shortage in cleaning supplies like Lysol and even some medical equipment like masks, gloves and face shields. I believe that many Americans subconsciously feared the thought of having to quickly change up their routine and isolate from each other.

The chaos didn't stop there, because we when we first learned of this virus, we were unsure about a lot of the details. Early on, we were told so many different things about the effects of the virus. At first, it wasn't known how one could contract coronavirus. There were speculations of it potentially being airborne that scared a lot of Americans. There was even a point when desperate Americans went to the extreme of drinking bleach in an attempt to prevent themselves from catching the virus.

Millions of businesses were forced to close because they were not deemed "essential". But even the essential businesses like grocery stores and doctor's offices had to immediately adjust their rules and operating hours. Then there were strict limitations put in place to regulate who could be on the roads after certain hours. If you didn't have the proper identification and authorization to be on the roads, local officials would enforce those restrictions.

The year of 2020 did not only introduce us to the novel coronavirus and its solitude, but also opened the door to isolation.

For many Americans, the mixture of both COVID-19 and mandated isolation was a difficult drink to digest.

I remember in early March, when the state of Georgia seemingly shut down for quarantine, for what was expected to be two weeks. Each day, there were new reports from state and local officials, as well as the Centers for Disease Control (CDC). The internet and social media were literally the best and worst places to be. On one end, there was so much information readily available to you, but on the other end, it was almost an overload of information, which made it hard to filter between facts and conspiracies. Half of the information that was being viewed as fact couldn't even be properly verified because of how new the virus and pandemic were.

Prior to quarantine, many members of the Black community were unfamiliar with and ill-equipped to handle isolation. For years, the Black community has normalized masking or hiding true emotions by attempting to remain constantly busy. Based on an article from the University of Georgia's Department of Psychology, avoidance is one of the symptoms of racial trauma, which is often experienced in the Black community. However, with the nationwide lockdown, many were forced to sit with their thoughts and manage their isolation. At the same time, others were forced to make difficult decisions involving work and their future economic standing.

Because I was raised by an educator, I will forever be a huge supporter of education and educators. But not everybody has the same respect for teachers. According to the *Digest of Educational Statistics*, in 2017 the average public-school teacher in the United States made $59,000. I would argue that teachers are very underpaid and underappreciated for the number of expected responsibilities. According to the *Global Teacher Status Index*, a survey that examines respect for teachers among the public in 35 countries, America ranking at No. 16 (Walker, 2018). While countries like China and Malaysia were top ranked because they view teachers as being on the same level as doctors. I wonder if America has more respect for teachers after 2020.

More importantly, it was disheartening to see how much added pressure was put on teachers to deliver the same quality of education, despite the quick transition. Teachers were expected to enrich kids with this "business as usual" mindset, while ignoring the fact that teaching had always been in-person because it yielded more efficient results. Unlike other professions or jobs that thrived with remote work, education was quite the opposite, and the fear of COVID-19 didn't help the situation.

EDUCATORS

"It was March 12th... that was the last date I wrote on the board. I didn't realize I wouldn't be stepping back into my classroom again", explained Ms. T. Williams, a 4th grade public school teacher from Georgia with an MA in Curriculum and Instruction.

On that day, every public school teacher in Georgia was informed of a statewide shelter-in-place order that would require quick adaptability and an immediate implementation of virtual learning. Ms. Williams had been working with low-income communities as an elementary school teacher for decades. From the chalkboard to the smartboard, she holds over 30 years of experience and has taught various curriculums throughout her educational career. However, even the most experienced teachers could not have predicted or been prepared for the historic shift to virtual learning.

According to data from the Pew Research Center and National Center for Education Statistics (NCES), during the 2015-2016 school year, racial and ethnic minorities accounted for 20 percent of all public elementary and secondary school teachers in the United States, compared to the 51 percent of all public elementary and secondary school students in the US who were non-White in 2015-16. Additionally, in 2017-18, only 7 percent of public-school teachers and 11 percent of public-school principals were Black. Yet, more than 15 percent of public school students nationwide are Black (National School Boards Association, 2020). So, it's evident that there has always been a unique yet obvious need for additional Black public-school educators to equally represent the amount of minority students involved.

Specifically, with lower income communities, the switch to virtual learning was more difficult than most anticipated. The biggest challenge that Ms. Williams had to address was the assumption that each student had access to the same resources. Some of her students did not have access to internet, while others dealt with difficult home circumstances out of their control. Parents who fell under essential worker classification or were fortunate enough to still be employed during the economic downfall, were also forced to make difficult decisions on where to leave their children while working.

Often the Black community and lower income areas tend to fall short when it comes to the proper distribution of funds and resources. Two-thirds of minority students still attend schools that are predominantly minority, most of them located in central cities and funded well below those in neighboring suburban districts (Darling-Hammond, 1998). I do not think anybody was prepared for the amount of stress that followed. It took multiple weeks during March to get begin to give the proper resources like Chromebooks and Wi-Fi hotspots to the communities in need. Ultimately, the responsibility fell on the shoulders of the principals and other administrators.

In the meantime, teachers were still responsible for ensuring the education of each and every student, including providing written copies of lessons and homework for students without internet access. Because of the lack of resources, written packets were left at the school for parents to pick up. But, because of COVID-19, the schools were only open for a short window of a few hours. Some parents reached out to Ms. Williams to let her know that they could not get the packet during the scheduled hours, due to work or other personal conflicts. This forced Ms. Williams and a lot of educators to become innovative with their solutions. Because Ms. Williams has a true love for her students and their education, she spent time gathering addresses of students who were still in need of work, in order to ensure that her students could still receive their schoolwork despite the circumstances.

Other times, her principal, Mr. Raymond Stanley, would take on the responsibility of delivering homework packages and WIFI hotspots to families in need during the pandemic. "You know we live [work] in a low-income community, and so many of our parents don't have [private] transportation. Sometimes they use public transportation or even Uber back and forth. So, when those requests come in from parents, I don't mind helping."

"Before the pandemic, we had not practiced giving out Chromebooks to our students, so it was an adjustment," confessed principal Raymond Stanley.

Additionally, he was responsible for communicating with and managing the concerns of his faculty, which was a large task in itself. In the spirit of transparency, Principal Raymond Stanley would communicate and send off multiple emails and notices that were receive from his superiors. He had to remain flexible due to the daily changes but also show confidence in the virtual transition, in order to help alleviate panic among his faculty. But having to juggle those emotions only aided to the stress and anxiety that he felt on a personal level.

After my conversation with principal Raymond Stanley, it was evident to me that the rapid changes at the beginning of quarantine clearly caused him some stress and anxiety. On a personal level, as a Black man, he told me he was familiar with the concept of "praying away" his problems. But in 2020, using his faith was not as effective as it once was.

He explained to me that even when he was off the clock, he didn't understand why he felt so much anxiety and stress. "It could be something small or big, but once it's on my mind, it's hard for me to get it off. Especially in the middle of the night or early in the morning, it can just sit there, you know?" expressed Raymond Stanley.

I felt that his anxiety and stress stemmed from a combination of pressure and stress from his work life and the impact of quarantine. Even though it seemed as though principal Raymond Stanley didn't experience any lasting effects of isolation because he was at the school and driving around, making deliveries for families, that wasn't the case. Sudden isolation still hindered his normal routine and caused him additional stress and anxiety.

Fortunately for Mr. Stanley, he found one activity that has remained a constant outlet for him, even throughout the isolation and pandemic... golfing. He has continued to use golfing as a stress relieving exercise, which has proved helpful for him during isolation.

Still, it seemed no one could understand the pressure and stress of sudden isolation and these changes more than teachers. On one hand, teachers were immediately immersed in virtual learning trainings platforms. They were quickly taught how to operate unfamiliar platforms like Zoom and Microsoft Teams and then were immediately expected to enforce its use. Let's not even begin to discuss having to teach young and easily distracted elementary school students how to use these new platforms for academic purposes. You would be surprised how frustrating and redundant it can be to teach kids how to find and join different class meetings throughout the day, while simultaneously attempting to enforce punctuality and discipline. For Ms. Williams, each day was filled new meetings with administrators and new rules from the school district. Every other hour, there were memos being received from superintendents and emails from parents. And yet, teachers were simultaneously feeling pressure from students and their parents.

At the beginning of quarantine, a typical workday for Ms. Williams was constantly busy and exhausting. Every morning, she would wake up by 7 am to check emails and messages from parents and administrators. By 8 am, she was online, ready to open her virtual classroom on Microsoft Teams and greet her students. On any given day, she would split her time between addressing questions and concerns from her students and parents and finding innovative ways to virtually enforce respect and discipline guidelines with her students. Between having to teach through a computer screen and having to communicate with other teachers via her cell phone, there was rarely a moment that Ms. Williams had to relax. There were even instances where she would encounter families that only had one working device in the home with multiple students forced to share.

By the end of the school day, around 2 pm, Ms. Williams had not moved from her computer screen. She then had to log into faculty meetings, just to ensure that she stayed updated on the ever-changing virtual learning environment. If she didn't have a meeting scheduled that day, her time would go toward reaching out to parents in order to update them on the academic or behavioral progress of their child. It was safe to say that at any given moment, Ms. Williams had to manage her stress level and always had to be prepare for the unexpected.

According to a *New York Times* article, COVID-19 has placed those same underpaid teachers at the heart of a national crisis, as the US looked to teachers not only for children's education and well-being but also as essential childcare while parents try to get back to work (Goldberg, 2020). It almost seemed as though parents were confused on the expected responsibilities of educators. This echoed one of the most frustrating feeling for Ms. Williams. She was constantly hearing critics and parents alike, question and downplay the workload and daily responsibilities of teachers. She dealt with parents who were unhappy with their child's academic and behavioral progress during the virtual learning transition while other parents who felt teachers weren't interacting enough on camera to properly educate.

"Personally, I do take extreme offense to [parents' expectations] because with 31 years of teaching, I do absolutely nothing but give my all. I mean, teaching is what I do. It's innate, it's who I am," Ms. Williams expressed. She and other teachers alike, went into the education profession because of their love and dedication to the betterment of future generations.

If that didn't seem like enough stress, the real nightmare for Ms. Williams set in when she closed her work laptop at the end of each workday. Her love for teaching has always been fueled by being able to engage and interact with students. However, the rapid switch to virtual learning left a gap in her internal happiness and exacerbated the feeling of isolation. When Ms. Williams closed her laptop, she had to deal with life as Tara Williams.

Tara Williams was trying her best at managing her new quarantine life. Even with both of her kids home from college because of the pandemic, the sudden shift of isolation was impacting her mental health. Tara was raised as an only child, and having both her kids living back home, she had never felt more isolated than in 2020.

"I remember being in my 20s. I had just started teaching in Brooklyn. I was on the train traveling to go somewhere, and I remember having [a panic attack]. It was so bad that my dad had to come help calm me down and get me off the train" explained Tara, as she reminisced on her what lead her to her first experience with a therapist.

After that incident, Tara spent the next year going to therapy and figuring out what triggered her anxiety and how she could best manage it. From there, she walked away with an understanding that the fear of the unknown tends to trigger her, but that certain breathing exercises could help.

However, it seemed as though the pandemic, isolation, and COVID-19 was bringing uncertainty and 'the fear of the unknown' full circle. Even though Tara, as an only child, had used her coping skills to deal with the death of both her parents years earlier, those same coping skills were not working this time.

"At the beginning of the lockdown, I won't lie; I definitely had a few panic attacks because I just didn't know when the pandemic would be over. I was worried about my underlying health condition and worried if one of my kids would get it or give it to me," discussed Tara.

The similarities and parallels between an overwhelmed Tara in her 20s, and an overwhelmed and uncertain Tara in 2020, is uncanny. But she convinced herself that she was too busy to professionally address these mental health issues she experienced during 2020. In between virtual learning and making sure her kids properly adjusted to the rapid switch, she felt she didn't have time.

But that didn't stop her from attempting to create her own solutions when she felt her mental wellness becoming uneasy.

"I'm not seeing a therapist, and maybe I should, but I have still been remaining positive, with positive thoughts. I force myself to call and talk with friends throughout the week and chew gum when I feel a panic attack approaching. That's how I deal with it," confessed Tara.

Imagine working non-stop in a new work environment, just to be judged by your superiors and critics continuously. Imagine dealing with work stress while being mandated to shelter-in-place by the government, during a global pandemic... with worries of pay cuts looming in the background. Can you imagine how much those circumstances would affect your mental health?

STUDENTS

The switch from in-person to virtual learning was received better by some students than others. Depending on the age and grade level of the student, there were different obstacles to address and navigate. However, for student living in a low-income area, the experience may be worse.

According to the National School Boards Association (NSBA), In fall 2017 45 percent of Black students attended high-poverty schools, compared with 8 percent of white students. This comes with its own set of challenges like lack of access and resources. Additionally, among Black 3 to 18 years old, 11 percent had home internet access only through a smartphone, compared with only 2 percent among Asian and 3 percent among White students, stated the NSBA article.

During the lockdown, there were students who were forced to juggle learning in class and helping take care of their siblings at home. There were other students that were once reliant upon school meals, struggling to figure out what to eat during the day. Some students were forced to work in unconventional environments. On an internal level, kids had to adjust to not seeing each other or having those in-person interactions with friends. They had to deal with the fact that proms and graduations would look different than they imagined.

All of these changes had an immediate impact on the mental health of students across the country. Based on a 2020 Mental Health America (MHA) report, 13 percent of youth (aged 12-17) report suffering from at least one major depressive episode (MDE) in 2020. Additionally, the number of youth experiencing Severe MDE increased by 121,000 from last year's dataset.

So, it is very apparent to me that isolation has had a definite impact on the youth and students alike.

Some experts say that virtual learning could be the future of obtaining an education. Ms. Williams understands that it will be most difficult to reach and motivate students in low-income communities because of their disadvantages and lack of resources. However, the success of virtual learning is possible in these communities, if there is an intentional effort and attention put into providing the needed technology while keeping the students motivated. Regardless of the work environment, teachers have continued to adapt to the ever-changing educational industry.

In addition to many members of low-income communities being ill-equipped to handle the switch to virtual learning, I truly believe that the definition of isolation changed after experiencing the rapid change of events in 2020. At one point, the impact of isolation seemed solely internal. Isolation and loneliness went hand in hand. However, the experience of Ms. Williams, her principal, and ultimately other students, illustrates that you can feel impact of isolation even if you talk through a screen every day. The quarantine showed that the signs and effects isolation can be disguised to look like stress, pressure, anxiety, and depression. Depending on your role in life, isolation no longer solely looks like *being* alone. It now has grown to include *feeling* alone due to the amount of pressure and stress you have.

Let's not forget about the mental effects and stress that teachers, administrators, and students dealt with? Can you see how the combination of virtual learning and sudden isolation can have an impact on public schools within low-income communities? How have education and isolation impacted you? When you reminisce about teaching and the educational transition in 2020, will you have a more empathetic understanding?

CHAPTER 5

Racism and Discrimination

"If you don't have a lens that's been trained to look at how various forms of discrimination come together, you're unlikely to develop a set of policies that will be as inclusive as they need to be"

—*KIMBERLE WILLIAMS CRENSHAW*

Summer 2020 was like no other for the African American community. At the beginning of the summer, the outrage for the deaths of George Floyd and Breonna Taylor sparked global protest. I believe the reason that the George Floyd incident became the tipping point for the world is the fact that millions of people sat helplessly and watched how he suffered in the last eight minutes and 46 seconds of his life. We all saw him repeatedly beg for his life. We heard him call out for his mother. And more importantly, we all witnessed the lack of human decency that he was shown in his last living moments. There was no ignoring how cruel and brutal those police officers were, as we unfortunately watched George Floyd's life slip away from us.

Shortly after that, we learned of the story of 25-year-old Black male, Ahmaud Arbery, killed for jogging in a Georgia neighborhood. At the same time in NY, a white woman went viral for falsely calling the cops on Christian Cooper, an unarmed Black man attempting to bird watch at the park. Not even a month after that, another unarmed Black male, Rayshard Brooks, was ultimately killed by police officers in a Wendy's parking lot. There was so much imagery around the killing and deaths of African Americans, that it quickly began to feel as though we were experiencing the same form of extreme racism and discrimination that our elders from the early Civil Rights era had fought against.

I've always felt like it was necessary to soak up and absorb different aspects of the Black history and our relationship with racism. I wanted to have a better appreciation and awareness for how much my ancestors sacrificed. Our elders had to live through the trauma of the lynching of 14-year-old Emmitt Till in the 50s and the brutal beating of Rodney King in the 90s. Yet I was constantly told by elders around me that my generation would never have to experience what they went through in terms of racial inequality. Well, I wonder what my elders would say now, after watching what our community endured during 2020?

Look, as a proud 90s baby (1996 to be exact), I completely understand that generations before me had to deal with slavery, segregation, and the fight for civil rights. I recognized that I never had those experiences. According to Mental

Health America, racism is a mental health issue because racism causes trauma. And trauma paints a direct line to mental illnesses, which need to be taken seriously. Past trauma is prominently mentioned as the reason that people experience serious mental health conditions today (Mental Health America, 2021).

Frankly, the first time I encountered blatant racism was in 2015 during my first year of college. I was visiting Panama City Beach, Florida with a few friends for spring break that year. We all went into a Walmart to pick up a few things. I found myself in a separate aisle than my friends, when I passed by an older white woman in her late 70s. She said, loudly enough for me to hear "move out the way, you nigger." In that moment, my entire body felt as though it was completely frozen from numbness, almost like an out-of-body experience. I really don't think it registered to me, at the moment, what had happened. I immediately left the aisle to go find my friends and tell them what happened. Of course, when they heard, they were ready to look through the store to find the woman, and while I appreciated their support, I didn't want to do that. I was still in shock and wanted to disappear. I felt small, unwanted, unwelcomed, and almost dehumanized. An 18-year-old me had not realized that one "little" word, had so much control and hurt associated with it, until I was put in the situation myself.

The fact that I never responded to that racist woman or stood up for myself and my ancestors, definitely still haunts me to this day. I never wanted to feel like I was taking my Black experiences for granted. Honestly, before 2020, I never thought I would ever be able to live through, let alone, tell similar stories about racism to my own future children one day. But here we are. Even after hearing and learning of the experiences of others, I believe it did not prepare me enough for the amount of direct racism that I witnessed in 2020 and how it would impact the mental health of the Black community.

"In conjunction with everything going on right now, it kinda feels like the chaos of 2014 with Michael Brown, all over again," explained Toni-Ann Hines, a Wake Forest law student with a BS in Psychology from Howard University. In 2014, Toni used protesting to help deal with the emotional stress that surrounded the killing of Michael Brown. Six months into 2020, she found herself triggered again by similar emotional traumas. Only this time, Toni was slowly becoming overwhelmed on every imaginable level.

As an immigrant from Jamaica and proud member of the LGBTQA+ community, Toni was having a hard time ingesting the continuous traumatic events that had occurred over that last few months. Twitter notifications came up constantly, informing her of the deaths of her idols Kobe Bryant and Katherine Johnson.

Experiences like those, accompanied by hearing the unfortunate but all too familiar, story of Nina Pop, had left her exhausted with emotion. Nina Pop was a 28-year-old black transgender woman who was violently assaulted and killed in Sikeston, Missouri. According to the Human Right's Campaign, Nina Pop was believed to be at least the tenth violent death of a transgender or gender non-conforming person in 2020 in the US (Elliot Kozuch, 2020).

On top of that, she had another concern stirring in the back of her head. From a health perspective, the coronavirus had affected her in a different way. Because she suffered from asthma, she was one of the many Americans, who was classified as having an increased risk for severe illness. According to the Center of Disease Control (CDC), people with moderate to severe asthma may be at higher risk of getting very sick from COVID-19. COVID-19 can affect your nose, throat, and lungs (respiratory tract); cause an asthma attack; and possibly lead to pneumonia and acute respiratory disease. These factors not only impacted her social life, but further aided the stressors of her mental wellbeing (Centers for Disease Control and Prevention, 2020).

Toni didn't really think she could handle any more trauma, but then she heard the news of Breonna Taylor.

"As a Black woman, I don't really have the words for it because I think we just understand that not only are we black, but we're woman, and being a black woman intersects and it just creates a new world of just chaos" stated Toni, as she remembered her initial thoughts when she heard the news about Breonna Taylor.

Breonna Taylor was a 26-year-old Black woman, who was shot multiple times and killed by Louisville, Kentucky police officers, while in her apartment on March 13, 2020. Unfortunately, her name didn't receive mainstream attention until early June, when it was mentioned alongside the death of George Floyd.

Toni felt more emotionally connected to the Breonna Taylor story than any other. It was infuriating to know that a black woman like Breonna Taylor, who was a medical worker and first responder during the pandemic, had been senselessly murdered by cops and still did not receive justice. It seemed like, at every turn, the public or critics had their own reasons or excuses for her death. As a community, knowing that there was no true protection for either Nina Pop or Breonna Taylor, triggered both an emotional and physical reaction from Toni. Fortunately for Toni, she had always been a proud BLM advocate and no stranger to protesting or engaging with the community. She had always found joy in educating others on the power of equality. Despite her unique health situation, which forced her to remain cautious, she had a need to fulfill.

Confined to her house, she spent the next few days reaching out to peers and allies alike to organize a small movement to help protestors on the frontlines in her hometown. Within 48 hours, she raised over $1,000 in donations and successfully created over 100 medical supply bags. For the frontline protestors who were encountering violence, the emergency supply bag was very helpful and included items like protective eyewear, a mask, small and large band-aids, gauzes, and alcohol wipes.

Toni felt as though she needed to do what she could to bring attention to Breonna Taylor's story. So, on June 3rd, with her health restrictions in consideration, Toni grabbed her mask, a friend, and created a stand on the sidelines of the protest from which she handed out supplies until she ran out. Being able to join the melodic chants of "say her name" while assisting other protesters, left Toni with a new sense of accomplishment that had been missing from the previous protest she had participated in. She couldn't imagine beginning Pride Month any other way.

Unfortunately, her positive feeling of accomplishment and pride was short lived. On June 8th, the news about the death of Dominique "Rem'Mie" Fells, a Black, transgender woman from Philadelphia, hit social media. Within the next 24 hours, a similar story broke explaining the traumatic death of Riah Milton, another Black, transgender woman from Ohio. According to *Times*, including Fells and Milton, there had been at least 14 transgender or gender non-conforming people killed in 2020 (Madeleine Carlisle,2020).

In the midst of a month that is normally filled with pride and celebration for the queer community, Toni was mourning and dealing with the PTSD of constantly seeing people who look like her, die. To make matters worse, by June 12, 2020, the Trump administration had also revoked transgender health protection. According to the Associated Press, the finalized rule from the Trump administration overturned Obama-era protections for transgender people against sex discrimination in health care (Ricardo Alonso-Zaldivar,2020).

The combination of these prominent, yet traumatic events not only left Toni numb, but the silence and lack of care from her peers seemed to negatively impact her the most. It was frustrating to witness the LGBTQA+ community continuously fight on the frontlines for the equality and inclusiveness of the Black community, and not receive the same kindness in turn. Where is the reciprocated energy for the LGBTQA+ community when they need it?

At some point, all these feelings became too much for her to handle. She had been self-isolating and crying off and on. But because of her background in psychology, she realized it was time to seek out additional help. Unfortunately, the coronavirus had also directly impacted the counseling industry, resulting in the chaotic emergence of telehealth.

"It was just weird. I felt like she was just there to problem-solve my situation, but I want my therapist to get in-depth and know how I really feel," explained Toni.

Oftentimes, the Black community can be hesitant to seek out counseling for many reasons. Like Toni's experience with telehealth, individuals want to feel like their issues are being heard. In Toni's case, she felt that her session was not intimate enough for her liking. There was not enough time spent to understand the true root of her problems. Oftentimes, it seemed like telehealth professionals tended to gauge their effort level and resources around how close a patient was to the extremes of suicide. This is unfortunate for the Black community, because they experience a great deal of trauma but received the short end of the resource stick.

The Black community often has a harder time properly articulating their problems and in general, can find it difficult to lower their guard around health care professionals. That can result in professionals not looking at these problems as severe enough to prioritize. A 2011 study from the National Center for Biotechnology Information about the exploration of Black patient experiences in initial mental health encounters explained that patients observe subtle cues during the interaction to make determinations about their provider's ability to be sensitive to their culture, thus implying that Black providers could be more culturally sensitive to Black patients. When patients talked about feeling safe enough to disclose personal information, they wanted to express themselves and tell their stories without being interrupted by providers. They also wanted to have the providers' attention as they freely shared personal or sensitive information (Earl & Linhart, 2011).

Toni did not feel prioritized during that moment and decided she would figure how to deal with her mental health struggle on her own. By the end of Pride Month, Toni felt mentally drained and emotionally exhausted. All she could think of doing next to fill her void, was to go dark on all her social media profiles and cleansing herself of the negative energy. But that didn't stop the traumatic events from rolling in.

On June 30th, the last day of Pride Month, the death of Merci Mack made the news. According to the Human Rights Campaign, she was a 22-year-old Black transgender woman in Dallas, Texas. Her death was believed to be at least the 18th known violent death of a transgender or gender non-conforming person this year in the US (Elliott Kozuch,202).

With no sense of help from the telehealth community and no sense of a vaccine in sight for her health concerns, Toni was forced to deal with these traumatic events on her own. She was left to replay these traumatic images and events in her brain for days on end.

After my conversation with Toni, I was interested in learning more about the LGBTQ community and specifically, the Black trans community, and how race and sexual orientation and preference impacted them in 2020.

This is how I came across Imara Jones' Instagram page. Imara Jones is a journalist and creator and founder of TransLash Media and podcast. Imara is also a proud member of the Black trans community and prides herself on telling and producing trans stories.

I found an Instagram posted from Imara dated July 13, 2020, with a picture that showed the title of an online article for the nonprofit organization, the Brady United read "73: Gun Violence and the Murder of Black Trans Women."

Imara'a caption below read: "Thank you @bradybuzz for having me on to discuss the ways in which Black transgender women are impacted by horrific gun violence. The impact on our [Black trans] community from guns used in intimate partner violence is often left out of public discourse. Black trans women have as much at stake as any group of people in the push for gun control" (Instagram, 2020).

I immediately began to empathize with the struggles of the Black trans community, in particular because I know what it feels like to feel unwanted as a Black person. I can only imagine how brave you have to be to live in your truth as a Black trans woman, where you can feel unwanted by the Black community and the LGBTQ community. I assume it only adds an extra layer of silence, trauma, and isolation to an already difficult journey through life.

As I continued down my Imara Jones rabbit-hole, I came across a think piece that Imara did for The Grio in 2020, during Pride Month. The title of the article was" Iyanna Dior's beating proves Black lives still don't matter if you're trans."

Iyanna Dior was from the Minneapolis-St. Pau area and unfortunately found herself badly beaten during Pride Month 2020, by a group of 20 or more Black men. I remember watching a viral video on social media of Iyanna Dior being trapped inside a convenience store by a large crowd of Black men who decided to yell threats at her, constantly misgendering her and repeatedly calling her a gay man. From the video, I remember Iyanna looked very scared as the screams and insults turned violent and I felt sick to my stomach watching.

Imara mentioned in her well-articulated think piece that, it is truly a bitter irony that many Black men, who are demanding to be seen as human beings, consistently eviscerate the humanity of others. The fact that tens of thousands of them are taking to the streets demanding an end to ignorance and fear, which can lead to murder, even as they perpetuate the same violence against Black trans women, is equally distasteful (Imara Jones, 2020).

I completely agree and empathize with the irony and unfair treatment of Black trans women, especially at the hands of Black men. As a Black woman who has experienced my fair share of unpleasant experiences with Black men, I can empathize with the confusion around whether Black trans women should show up for those same Black men who are killing them at an astounding rate, and who overwhelmingly do not show up for them. I battle with those exact thoughts sometimes as well.

I can only imagine how exhausting those daily battles can be on the physical and mental health of Black trans women and other members of the LGBTQ community. Unfortunately, this is the constant mental and physical cycle that most people in the black community go through when they are constantly bombarded with negative images and traumatic media stories, with no real help or solution in sight. They offer to sit with these ideas and suffer in silence, hoping a day will come by, where the pain won't be as strong anymore.

But on a more broad and basic level, racism continues to impact the mental health of the Black community. Whether it be through traumatic images constantly be shown in the media or through the lived encounters with racists, it is time to acknowledge that racism is a mental health issue that needs to be properly addressed.

CHAPTER 6

Black Male Trauma is Real

"Out of your vulnerbilities, will come your strength."
— SIGMUND FREUD

As the older sister to a 19-year-old young Black man, I share the same fears and worries as any Black woman who has a relationship with a Black male.

I constantly worry for the safety of my brother every time he's out of sight. Will he make it home safely? Is he afraid to live? Because sometimes I'm afraid for him. Is the outside world treating him with humanity, or as a stereotype? When other people see him, what do they see? Because what I see is a young fragile soul, one who is constantly fighting internally to remain resilient, strong, and determined, despite battling with silenced generational traumas and daily pressure from society. But frankly, I think he's doing a damn good job, given his limited amount of resources.

I will be the first to admit, even though my brother and I were both raised under the same roof for years, we ultimately lived two totally different lives. From our hobbies and our personalities to everyday personal experiences, it's really fascinating when I think about how opposite we have grown to be. Regardless, we have always shared a very unique bond. I can admit that even though he's five years younger than me, he has experienced way more trauma in his short years than I have. Unfortunately, I feel that his experience directly reflects the effects of the compounding pressures of society.

I will never forget waking up to the screams and cries of my little brother a week before his 18th birthday. I could hear his quick, yet explosive shriek from the next room over. The sound of his screams of shock mixed with cries of disbelief is a noise that is etched in my memory forever. For me, that sound is forever synonymous with traumatic death.

I remember immediately holding my brother in my arms as he wept for the sudden and violent death of his high school football teammate, or as he would say "brother," who fell victim to senseless gun violence.

"I fell asleep and an hour later, I woke up to a missed call from him and messages in the group chat asking if I had heard what just happened... and literally since then life has been so crazy," explained, my brother Miles, as he struggled to reminisce and articulate the exact moment he found out about the tragic death of one of his closest high school friends.

Before the age of 18, my brother had experienced three different traumatic deaths, but I could tell this one would have a lasting effect on him. It seemed like the final straw that broke the mental health camel's back. He blamed himself for missing the call and constantly asked himself various "what if" questions. He remembered feeling confused, upset, hurt, and numb all at the same time. He took a step back from friendships and even had moments where he attempted to isolate himself from the family. It was obvious to me that he was completely broken and lost in that moment but never felt like he had the time or even deserved the privilege to unpack his feelings.

At that moment, I didn't realize that he was actively living through different stages of grief. But his actions toward me and others showed denial, anger and depression. That is the main reason I became active in the mental health space: because it was really hard watching my brother suffer without having resources in place or proper knowledge to help. In that moment, I didn't know where to turn for help.

According to the National Institute of Health (NIH), in addition to premature death, homicide also places Black males at disproportionate risk for experiencing the traumatic loss of a peer and becoming homicide survivors. Homicide survivors are the friends, family, and community members of homicide victims who face the task of living on after a loved one is killed (Smith, 2015). However, this term is not normalized within the Black community, and there are a lack of resources offered in our communities that specialize in traumatic experiences and homicide survivors. The obvious lack of mental health resources in Black communities is oftentimes why members of the Black communities attempt to normalize themes like PTSD, anxiety and depression.

To be quite frank, Black men in America move closer to extinction every day. Statistically speaking, Black men live seven years less than men of other racial groups and also have higher death rates than Black women for all leading causes of death (Kennard, 2020). According to gun statistics at Gifford's Law Center, Black men make up 52 percent of all gun homicide victims in the US, despite comprising less than 7 percent of the population. So, I consider Black males to be one of the most preyed on demographics in America.

When I started writing this book, I knew it would be more important than ever to vocalize the silenced traumas and experiences of the Black man.

DEATH BRINGS TRAUMA

Death is never an easy topic to discuss, and it seems like no matter your age, death can have a lasting impact.

I can vividly remember the moment a dark death cloud began to loom over me. I was in the 5th grade and had to leave school for a few days, which was unusual for me, the queen of perfect attendance. I flew to New York to visit my grandmother who was in the hospital, sick with cancer. I didn't realize it then, but that would be the last time my life would feel normal.

At 9 years old, I couldn't find the right words to express my thoughts and emotions but looking back, I realize that I had my first dances with death and depression. Looking back, I realize that I was dealing with a great deal of grief over the death of my grandmother. But more importantly, I witnessed my mom attempt to deal with grief, depression, and PTSD, all while trying to maintain her career, the household, and her children.

As I got older, I truly realized just how much she handled on her own. Like most of the Black community, we are forced to learn how to manage grief and death on our own. As a community, we find ourselves attempting to function like normal in order to drown out uncomfortable feelings. There is often a fear of "showing weakness," which continues to add to the stigmas in our community. We feel like we constantly have to show that we can be strong in the face of oppression, which is why over the years, mental health hasn't taken a position of priority in the Black community.

More than often, members of the Black community are introduced to the mental health effects of death early in life without the proper tools to handle it. Sadly, death is a recurring theme in the community and can have a crippling impact on generations. For Black males, in particular, it is almost inevitable that they will have experience with death or gun violence. According to findings at the CDC, in 2017, the leading cause of death in Non-Hispanic black males, between the ages of 20 and 44 is homicide (CDC, 2017). In addition to premature death, homicide places Black males at disproportionate risk for experiencing the traumatic loss of a peer and becoming homicide survivors (CDC, 2017).

For 24-year-old Derrick Johnson, those same statistics were the driving force for him to create his non-profit in the mental health field. He has continued to use his non-profit, BROStigmas, to destigmatize mental health awareness in the Black community and among Black males in particular.

Derrick's passion for mental health in the Black community began in undergrad at Grambling State University, where he worked overnight with less-fortunate children at a group home. He found himself wanting to help his community overcome generational obstacles and adversities, and he began focusing on mental health.

Like most Black men in 2020, Derrick noticed that the theme of death was really big during the year. From hearing the untimely death announcements of historical and influential figures like John Lewis, Kobe and Chadwick Bosman, to opening social media and seeing other Black males like George Floyd tragically being murdered, the year was undoubtedly difficult for Black men.

"This year was a constant trigger for me, almost reminding me of middle school" explained Derrick as he reflected on how 2020 impacted his mental health. "I say that because of the self-isolation, a lot of those depressive thoughts came back in my head in 2020".

Derrick Johnson has dealt with the theme of traumatic deaths since a young age. During his middle school days, he lost both his father and uncle to suicide within a year of each other. In the blink of an eye, his life was changed forever as he was thrust into manhood at a young age, attempting to fill the void of left by his father. With a single mom and siblings at home, a young Derrick immediately felt pressure. Both of those deaths left him with unanswered questions, confusing emotions, and in a depressive state. As a child with these unnamed thoughts, he would often self-isolate, listening to music that reminded him of better times with his dad and letting various unanswered questions run around his head.

Unlike most Black males who are faced with their first traumatic death experience, Derrick was able to seek out mental health resources in the form of therapy to address it. Over the next three years, he went to weekly sessions where he learned how to properly cope with death, triggers, and learned that there were great benefits of journaling.

"I'm big on the idea that if you look like me, then we can relate," stated Derrick when explaining the importance of having a Black male therapist at such a young age. According to the American Psychology Association, in 2015, 86 percent of psychologists in the US workforce were white, 5 percent were Asian, 5 percent were Hispanic, 4 percent were Black/African American, and 1 percent were multiracial or from other racial/ethnic groups (Lin & Stamm, 2018). There is a certain level of comfort that most people feel when they can speak with someone who looks like them. Unfortunately, there are not enough African American professionals in the industry, which is just the tip of the iceberg problem. The bigger issue is the problem of access and dispersion to underserved communities, which adds to the many disparities within the mental health care system.

Derrick found himself triggered, almost feeling like a middle school boy again as he attempted to cope with the recent death of another uncle, Michael Murrell, who passed away due to complications from COVID-19.

"I found myself really getting in a depressed mode, so I needed to get out and take a break throughout the day," explained Derrick. Luckily because of his prior experiences with therapy and mental health, Derrick was able to vocalize, recognize, and properly address his feelings. Compared to his middle school self, this time Derrick realized that the death of his uncle was triggering, so he was immediately able to talk himself through his negative thoughts. He realized which tools worked best for him and remained consistent with using them. In therapy, he'd learned his triggers and which exact tools or solutions helped in a particular moment.

Because Derrick would describe himself as a very social and outgoing person, the isolation of having to quarantine during the year impacted his normal coping techniques like hanging out and interacting with friends. Based on his personal experience with therapy and his understanding of mental health, Derrick decided to use journaling and daily walks as the best practices to cope with the triggers of 2020.

"I feel like journaling is a big thing, and I took it for granted when I was younger. I used to think that I didn't need to write this down, I could just talk to my homeboy and get through it but that's not the case," explained Derrick.

I have always been a big fan of journaling. For me, there has always been something soothing about being able to write out your feelings and being having the option to reflect and read back those feelings later. Journaling is often used as a therapeutic tool for people who may have a hard time vocalizing feeling. Oftentimes for males who battle with the stigmas of "not showing emotions," journaling can provide a sense of comfort, security, and vulnerability that can have beneficial long-term effects.

Regardless of which technique is used, there is a true benefit to having a basic understanding of mental health and its impact in your life. In Derrick's case, even though he only had a therapist in middle school, he was able to reiterate and apply certain coping skills he learned when needed. When compared to others within the Black community, Derrick is a part of a small minority of African Americans who have had the luxury of using mental health resources during their lifetime. When you have the proper tools to navigate your personal mental health journey, you find it easier to recognize and address stressors and triggers in your life.

In contrast with Derrick's 2020 experience, his friend and co-founder of BROStigmas, Cletus Empokae, had a very different experience. He experienced some of the same themes and triggers and extreme trauma, but as a Black man under constant pressures, he decided to use a less conventional method when faced with adversity.

PRESSURE BRINGS TRAUMA
There is a constant amount of pressure put on individuals in the Black community. As a community, we feel the pressure to suppress our emotions, but highlight our education, talents, and abilities. We feel the societal stress to dispel certain racial biases in and out of the workplace. Let us not forget, there is a force to flourish in a society that has been systematically designed to oppress.

Now, let's factor in the personal stressors. As a Black woman, one of the most recurring pressures I find in my life is mastering the art of being assertive. I have to walk a very thin line between femininity and independence or there's a chance that my actions could be misunderstood. Then, there is the pressure to show strength at every encounter with adversity. Not to mention, the intended sacrifice and looming difficulty of motherhood.

Yes, at some point, everyone comes face to face with pressure and stressors. However, for the Black community, there have been years of systematic oppression that have hindered generations from properly addressing and managing these issues. Can you imagine what four hundred plus years of generational pressures can do to an individual? The lack of education, wealth, equality, and basic human rights completely has hindered the African American community. That amount of pressure can only stay bottled up for so long before it eventually has no choice but to combust.

For Cletus Emokpae, a 26-year-old doctoral student and communications instructor at Howard University, there was no ignoring the compounded pressures of 2020. Cletus had spent the beginning months of the year heavily stressed. He was unhappy at his job, felt overworked and under-compensated, and was ultimately becoming exhausted with juggling both his professional life and his personal life. According to research, African American men experience severe effects in their work life like chronic stress and pressure more often—37.2 percent compared to 28.9 percent among Whites—as well as in their relationships (Neighbors, 2019). Black men often find themselves overwhelmed with constant pressure but rarely get to handled it properly.

"I felt like the weight of the world was on my shoulders, and I had to make things happen. I had to stay strong for my family, for myself, and still had to get things done in terms of deadlines and expectations," explained Cletus.

As a Staten Island native by way of Nigeria, he constantly felt societal and cultural pressure to succeed and protect and provide for his family in all aspects of his life. He understood the expectations from his family and felt like there was no choice but to succeed. In addition to his educational accomplishments, Cletus held other responsibilities. At the beginning of 2020, while fighting for racial equality within his workplace, he also spent time managing independent musical artists and helping his friend Derrick, as the co-founder of the BROStigmas nonprofit.

In his personal life, Cletus noticed that his so-called "friends" were having a hard time watching and supporting him through his success. He felt like these childhood friends were beginning to find hate and jealousy within his accomplishments. Coming from the Staten Island neighborhood that Cletus grew up in, not many Black men his age could say that they accomplished his level of education and professional goals.

However, Cletus was always proud to admit that he worked hard to defy the odds and accomplish his goals. It's just unfortunate that the same friends that he looked to as a support system completely changed how Cletus approached the rest of 2020.

What started as a mildly chaotic day for Cletus quickly transformed into a life-changing experience after he fell victim to an attempted homicide.

Cletus had spent the early part of his day at his corporate workplace dealing with microaggressions from other faculty members. He was still dealing with the unspoken grief of losing one of his biggest inspirations, Kobe Bryant. As a New York native, the sudden violent death of 20-year-old New York rapper, Pop Smoke, had also been affecting him indirectly. By the time he was finished with his workday, he had made plans with his friends to go out and celebrate Pop Smoke Day in the city.

Cletus had been looking forward to going out and partying with the guys, but that excitement quickly turned into confusion and soon anger, as he knocked on the door where he thought he was meeting his friend. When the door opened, he was then instructed by a guy to go around the back. But for Cletus, something just didn't feel right, so he chose to go home instead.

Luckily, he acted when he did because he was later informed by a friend about an intended plot, or "hit," on his life. It was in that same conversation that Cletus could only conclude someone truly had ill intentions for him. He didn't know who or why, but he knew he would have to address these uncomfortable feelings at some point.

The feeling of anxiety that trauma or violence could be around the corner, is a feeling that a lot of Black men can relate to. When you grow up as a Black man, there is a fear that trauma or even death can follow.

Like a lot of black men who have experienced a great deal of trauma, Cletus seemed to carry a sense of anxiety and apprehension when he walked up to the door. He could sense that something felt off and ultimately decided to take himself out of the situation.

Oftentimes, just the mere thought of trauma can impact how a person operates and sees themselves in the world. For Black men, activities that should be simple, like throwing on a hoodie or jogging alone in a neighborhood, become complicated because of their traumatic results.

"Why am I here? Why am I dealing with all this shit that I just shouldn't have to deal with? Why am I getting disrespected?" questioned Cletus as he remembered his exact thoughts in that eye-opening moment. He never truly understood where the hate or animosity from his so-called "friends" came from at that moment.

Everything seemed to happen so quickly that it wasn't until Cletus made it back home that he had time to truly reflect on what had just transpired. Even though Cletus had been told by his so-called friends to go to that particular apartment, he quickly realized that there was a good chance his "friends" set him up. But honestly, it was hard for him to comprehend that. The more Cletus reflected, the more he began to get comfortable with the idea that his friends were simply haters.

What Cletus would define as "haters," others may define as someone suffering from the "crab-in-a-barrel" mentality. This mentality occurs when people who come from the same environment or adverse circumstances as you, try to hinder your success and acceleration by attempting to keep you stagnant in the same situation or "barrel" as them. I like to look at it as "misery loves company." Cletus was realizing that his "friends" did not have good intentions for him.

That night, Cletus stayed up and reflected and replayed the events from that night. So many emotions and feelings traveled through his mind, but ultimately the feelings of hurt, anger, and trauma loomed. Oftentimes, men end up pushing those feelings so far down that they are replaced with a wall of anger and aggression.

"I realize that the reason why people disrespect me is because the love I have enables them to hate, so I snapped and really started to come at everybody," explained Cletus. He felt the best way to handle his trauma was to unleash this monster or new persona that would be tough enough to hide his true emotions. Unfortunately, in Cletus' situation, he unleashed this monster as a defense mechanism on any and everybody around him, whether they truly deserved the aggression or not. He went to confront his "friends" and even exchanged a few ill words with his attempted shooter. He began to walk around with an aggressive chip on his shoulder, vowing to never let another person catch him vulnerable like that again.

Any close brush with death reminds us of the precariousness and fragility of life and can strip away the layers of psychological suppression that shield us from uncomfortable thoughts of existential oblivion (Koch, 2020). For most, these events fade in their intensity with time, and normality eventually reasserts itself (although they may leave post-traumatic stress disorder in their wake) (Koch, 2020).

Personally, when I listened to him tell his story, I felt like he had a lot of misplaced anger in that moment that ultimately was taken out on those around him. But in order to provide him empathy in that moment, I actively listened to his experience. I never shared my opinions and instead let him feel comfortable enough to share his encounter. Like most Black men that found themselves attempting to deal with silence traumas, anger and aggression seem to be the easiest emotions to display. And I completely understand his frustrations and wish more people grasped that a lot of the "aggression" that is seen from Black men, is really just trauma that can present itself in a frustrated manner.

How is his voicing an opinion over being unjustly endangered different from protests about unjust killings? Are they not both murders or cries to not kill innocent people? Do we not expect justice for both? I wish more people grasped the concept that the "aggression" seen from Black men is really just trauma presented in a frustrated manner.

For anybody that has come that close to death, there is no doubt that they deal with trauma or have post-traumatic stress disorder (PTSD) that can be triggered by anything. For Cletus, because he had experience working with BROStigmas, he quickly realized that unleashing his "monster" was only a temporary fix. So, a few weeks later, he ultimately decided it was best to move away from Staten Island and focus on himself.

When I asked Cletus what stopped him from seeking out additional mental health resources like therapy or telehealth, he responded "Everyone's therapy is different, and I think we need to normalize that."

For Cletus, his therapy came in the form of traveling. Even though, due to the pandemic, he wasn't able to travel as much as he wanted, he was able to travel from Staten Island to see his family, and that made all the difference. However, according to the National Institute of Health (NIH), findings suggest that 56-74 percent of Black males exposed to traumatic events may have an unmet need for mental health services (Motley & Banks, 2018).

There are many ways to cope with pressure and stress. Some people may feel better by journaling, listening to music, traveling, seeking friendships, dancing, or meditation. However, for some members of the Black community, who have experienced continuous trauma and can't even vocalize the feelings of PTSD or triggers, they may need to seek out mental health resources and professional guidance to begin to understand the mental health basics. With the basic understanding of your triggers, the impact of trauma and effective coping techniques, the Black community can then see whether their methods of coping are truly effective, or if there is a better way to handle it.

So, with all that in mind, how are you judging Black men when you see them now? Are you taking into consideration the pressure and anxiety that they are walking around with? Or are you adding to the pressure? The next time you interpret anger and aggression from a Black male, take a second to consciously reflect in the moment. Can you begin to look at the situation with a more empathetic lens before reacting or responding?

Black men in America are a dying breed, one that is constantly dealing with pressure from society, work, family, and friends. They have been conditioned to show no weakness but at the same time, have experienced more compounding trauma than the majority of their racial counterparts. They are forced to watch other Black males be killed at the hands of police while being told their aggression is threatening.

There is an evident gap in the Black community when it comes to who is afforded proper access to mental health services. When Black men experience trauma or unnerving emotions, there is practically nowhere they can go to feel heard or seen. They often misplace those feelings and get quickly labeled with terms like "angry" or "thug." But these are not "thugs."

These are fragile and damaged souls that are constantly trying to navigate through the tough world with minimum resources. Black male trauma is real, so let's keep that in mind the next time you discuss or judge the Black male experience. To truly understand that Black male trauma is real is to truly see the Black male experience through a more empathetic lens.

CHAPTER 7

Coping

___

"You can only truly begin to cope when you learn to change your response to negative feelings and thoughts... in a positive way."
—TIARA JOHNSON

The constant stress of 2020 was, frankly, getting the best of me. Spending months navigating a shelter-in-place order, being in school virtually full-time, living back at home with family, and spending my free time filling out job applications were getting too mundane. More importantly, I was forced to isolate from friends and activities that I would normally use to cope. And I was slowly reaching my breaking point.

Pre-pandemic, if I needed to cope, I would easily find comfort in going out to eat, going the movies, or even a relaxing night out with friends. But with a shelter-in-place order in effect and majority of businesses closed, I had to search for a new way to cope and deal with my problems.

Because I was unemployed, I didn't have access to insurance benefits that would help me obtain mental health resources.

Luckily, being a student came with a few benefits, so I finally gathered up enough courage to begin the process of seeking out mental health resources that were offered through my university. For the past few months, I had recognized that I had feelings of hopelessness about the racial division in the country. There were constant thoughts running through my mind that I could not seem to compartmentalize. The emotional and mental stress was becoming overwhelming, and I recognized that I needed to talk to someone else who would be better equipped to help me sort out these feelings, in hopes that therapy could be my new form of coping.

I immediately began to do research to figure out what mental health resources were available for me and like most Americans in 2020, I was given the opinion of telehealth. Because my entire master's program had swiftly transition to virtual learning, access to mental health resources like counselors shifted too. According to market research conducted by Aritzon Advisory and Intelligence, the US telehealth market is expected to reach to around $10 billion in revenue by 2020 with high double-digit growth of around 80 percent, due to the recent COVID-19 pandemic (Aritzon Advisory and Intelligence, 2020). With the quick growth of the telehealth industry, it can be assumed that there may be some intentional gaps or missed opportunities.

For starters, there have already been some noted systematic gaps within the mental health space like lack of access to resources and lack of representation. Suddenly, we have this rapid immergence to telehealth, which grew as a result of the pandemic. However, these existing gaps have not been properly addressed; they have simply found another home in the telehealth industry.

I was nervous at the mere thought of being expected to bare my deepest internal thoughts and feelings with a potential stranger. However, I was more intrigued to talk with a professional that would finally be able to help me work though these emotions. I was able to get in contact with a faculty member in the counseling services offices whom I thought would help me schedule an official appointment. But I was mistaken.

Upon our first conversation, I told her I was hoping to find a counselor to help talk through some feelings and thoughts that I had been dealing with since the news of the killings of Breonna Taylor and George Floyd gained national attention.

"On a scale of 1-10, how often do these thoughts turn dark or suicidal?" she immediately responded.

"Not often at all, I'm really more worried that these feelings are just becoming more difficult to process on a daily basis," I informed her.

Without any additional follow-up or hesitation, it seemed that she had made an assessment to determine whether my issues would take priority. In a monotone voice, she announced to me that due to the high-volume of people in need of counseling services and lack of counselors to meet the demand, one-on-one sessions could not be offered. "However, you could look into group sessions that are available through Zoom," she advised. I felt completely dismissed and disregarded in that moment. I ended the call more discouraged than before. It seemed like I had a long road ahead of me on my mental health journey, but I was determined to seek help through any means. I was off to find a new coping method on my own.

It hurt to know that just because my "symptoms" or feelings didn't meet the criteria to be considered critical, I wasn't offered the option of one-on-one counseling that I expected. That feeling of dismissiveness is very familiar in the Black community. Oftentimes, as a community, our struggles, adversities, and feelings are dismissed by others because they lack true understanding and empathy. It really frustrated me because, if more therapists dealt with patients earlier on, as a preventative measure, then I feel that less patients would make it to the more critical or "suicidal" level. I felt that my experience or feelings were not being understood or valued properly which impacted my belief in the mental health/telehealth industry.

On one end, I was left completely discouraged, but on the other end, I ultimately felt the best way to cope was to submerge myself in Black mental health advocacy so that I can ensure other people have better first-time experiences than I did.

As a woman, I've always found it interesting to think about how men and women within the black community differ in their views about seeking out mental health resources. When interviewing two long-term friends with highly successful corporate positions, it was fascinating to analyze how both professionals discussed their opinions on mental health and coping methods.

ANDREA'S STORY

Andrea Hazzard and Everett Johnson sparked their 30-year friendship in the late 80's on the campus of Wagner College in Staten Island. Andrea graduated with a BS in microbiology, then a Master of Business Administration, and finally a law degree. Everett went on to graduate with a Business and Computer Science degree and entered the technology industry as a programmer. Both friends had spent years building very successful careers for themselves, but 2020 made them address other aspects of their personal lives.

Andrea Hazzard had spent the last 15 years of her career in the healthcare industry, working with internal business owners to ensure that their area of business remains compliant with federal programs. But the compounding events of 2020 were affecting her mental health. In addition to juggling her own anxieties, Andrea also has a daughter who suffers from bipolar disorder, which impacts the whole family.

"The whole mental health thing touches me so intimately. Because of the things that are going on with my daughter, it is very important for me to take care of myself so I can make sure that she is good," expressed Andrea.

Between having to continuously ingest traumatic news while managing the mental health of herself and her daughter, Andrea realized that it was becoming too much for her to handle. Although she and her daughter had been using telehealth resources since March 2020, things had gotten so intense that she was attending meetings weekly.

"It is important for me to recognize that sometimes it's okay for me not to be okay and to not wallow in that, but just to say 'you know what? You don't feel good and that okay,'" explained Andrea. She admitted that over the years, therapy has taught her the true value of mental health resources. Now she knows how to find healthy ways of coping with stress and depression and when to acknowledge that she needs additional help. One of her favorite coping methods was taking a moment to do breathing exercising and taking a moment out of the week for self-relaxation.

Personally, in the Black community, I think women are more likely to seek out mental health resources over men because we are more comfortable with our feelings and emotions. We understand when something feels off, and we have an easier time articulating our feelings. As Black women, we grow up understanding that we are supposed to emulate the strength of other matriarchs in our families. Sometimes that same strength is one of the reasons women can be hesitant to confront their mental health. But ultimately, in order truly embody the "strong Black woman" role for your family, you have to address certain issues and find the needed answers. This is why Andrea made it a priority to attend weekly sessions during 2020. She wanted to ensure that she could be that strong Black woman and role model for her family.

EVERETT'S STORY

However, as a Black man, Everett's story and experience with mental health resources is different.

Everett spent the last 20 years in various leadership roles at some of the country's top financial services firms. At his company, he leads software development, essentially spending time helping firms make decisions about how they plan to leverage technology. At a quick glance of his congested workload, you would never assume the amount of emotional and mental stress he was under in his personal life.

At the beginning of the year, Everett found out that lost the vision in his right eye. "That was really, really, tough to deal with emotionally. And I think that was the only point this year that I thought about 'well you know, maybe I should talk to somebody about it.' But then I was like 'no I'm not gonna do that,'" said Everett in a discouraging tone.

"As of right now, I have no vision in my right eye at all," explained Everett Johnson as he began to reflect on how this traumatic experience of 2020 impacted his mental and emotional health.

What started off in January as a seemingly minor issue with not seeing out of one eye properly, quickly escalated into a life-changing experience for him. When Everett first reached out to his eye doctor, he was initially diagnosed with a torn retina. It wasn't until he was coincidentally referred to another doctor from a different practice a few days later, that his injury was properly diagnosed as an actual detachment of the retina.

Because of the severity of the injury, Everett was scheduled for surgery within 72 hours. When he went to the consultation with his doctor, they discussed different surgery options. Everett explained that normally, when there is a repair to a detached retina, they'll put an air bubble in the eye between the retina and the eye while it's healing. When you use air, the air will dissipate after a two to three weeks. The only problem with using the air method is if you're going to fly, there's a possibility that the pressure from the airplane could cause the bubble to expand and that wouldn't be good.

The other option was to use a silicone oil instead. According to the August 2018 issue of *Retina Today Journal*, unlike gas, silicone oil remains in the eye until it is surgically removed and thus may be beneficial for inferior detachments or in patients who are unable to cooperate with postoperative positioning requirements. Additionally, silicone oil volume is unaffected by atmospheric pressure, so it may be used in patients who must undertake high altitude travel (Tyring, MD, 2018). The only downside of the silicone oil was that doctors would have to go back in to take it out after the eye is healed.

Everett had already made plans to fly to Queens, NY later that week, to check in on his mother and ultimately decided that the silicone alternative worked better for his situation. He was comfortable making the decision to remove the silicone oil at a later date because it allowed him the chance to take care of mom as the pandemic started to take hold.

Ironically, his later date. ended up being the week in March, when things started to shut down because of COVID-19. Nobody was prepared for how hard COVID-19 hit, and in St. Louis, where Everett lived, the number of cases had begun to increase quickly. During that week, the hospitals shut down all non-essential surgeries and considered the removal of his silicone oil to be not essential. A study was conducted by the University of Washington and the results projected that 28.4 million elective surgeries worldwide would be cancelled or postponed in 2020, with less than 30 percent of scheduled elective surgeries taking place (Nodell, 2020). Thanks to the pandemic, Everett, like millions of other Americans in 2020, was forced to postpone the surgery.

Three weeks later, Everett was finally able to see a doctor about his procedure to remove the silicone oil. That's when the doctor noticed that the pressure in the eye was much higher than it should be. Luckily, he was able to get Everett on the schedule for surgery within the next few days to address the issue.

The surgery happened, with everything seeming fine. However, when Everett woke the next day and took the bandage off, he couldn't see out of his right eye.

A concerned Everett immediately called his doctor and was told it could be that the nerve block that had been used in the surgery hadn't worn off yet. This left Everett anxious to see better results the next day. Unfortunately, when he woke up to the same results, his doctor told him to come in to run a test.

"I don't know how to say this to you. But the vision in your eye is gone," said the doctor.

"What do you mean? It's gone?" responded a confused Everett.

"There's really nothing that we can do. Our only hope is that maybe over time, it could come back. But with that amount of, you know, blood vessels that have no activity, the likelihood of that is, is very, very slim," explained his doctor.

Because Everett had always seen himself as a computer-oriented person, things needed to logical and equal out for him to understand them. He had a challenging time understanding the news that he had just received from his doctor. He had never been an overly emotional person, but the life-altering news left him silent for a few minutes. From there, he got up from his seat, walked out of the room, and headed for the parking lot in order to process this information as best he could.

It turned out that either during the surgery or sometime after the surgery, maybe during the night, Everett had a spike in pressure in the optic nerve that lasted long enough to cut off the blood flow to his eye. Once you cut off the blood flow, it could it kill the blood vessels in the retina. With these cases, it is something that should be caught within 45 to 90 minutes to have a chance of stopping it from causing permanent damage. Unfortunately, Everett's issue went untreated for two days.

The unexpected loss of his eyesight really took an emotional toll and frustrated Everett. It had never really crossed his mind that one of the outcomes would be not having vision. It wasn't until Everett spent that first night just sitting in a recliner with the lights out, that it all hit him, and he cried like a baby.

For the next few days, he continued to have those moments where he found himself having trouble holding back emotions. Crying was unusual for him, but he couldn't hold it in. He went through phases where he would question why this happened to him. He would replay memories in his head, where he felt he took his vision for granted. All these actions had a direct impact on his mental health.

For the next two months, Everett would wake up hopeful, thinking that this would be the morning his eyesight would come back. But nothing changed, and Everett had to begin to adjust to his new reality. Everyday tasks like driving and determining the depth perception of other traveling cars now had a different meaning for Everett.

"It was the first time that I flirted with the idea of getting some professional help to kinda talk through it," explained Everett. "I came close to doing it, and I didn't. But I think what happened is I had family that really stepped up and they were there for me."

Everett admitted that he would have been more inclined to seek out a professional if he wasn't fortunate to have the support system he did. Not only did Everett have immediate family members around to help lift his spirits at times, but he also had reconnected with old college friends like Andrea, which provided him with an additional support system. Because of the quick shutdown and immediate quarantine of the country, Everett, Andrea, and about 10 other old college friends found the time to reconnect for the first time in more than 30 years, thanks to the power of Zoom. What started out as one Zoom call to reunite, quickly escalated into weekly zoom meet-up that not only provided relief to Everett, but to others on the call as well.

The trauma from this event played a large part in the mental well-being and mental health journey of Everett. For the millions of other people who are not as fortunate to have a support system like Everett's, it's so critically important that people recognize mental health resources as legitimate options available to them, not as a last resort, but as a real option that can provide beneficial tools. Luckily, Everett decided to cope with his new reality by surrounding himself with supportive family and friends. He did not isolate himself and instead he reached out and embraced the support of others, which any professional therapist would note as a positive coping method.

Unfortunately, Everett's story of being ignored, under-prioritized, and potentially misdiagnosed within the medical field, is one to which most members of the Black community can relate. According to a Healthline online article, 12 million people in the US are affected by medical diagnostic errors each year, with women and minorities being 20 to 30 percent more likely to be misdiagnosed (Healthline.com, n,d). Not only can these racial biases and lack of care have lasting physical effects, but also lasting mental and emotional effects that can quickly blossom into trauma and PTSD.

"I'd be lying if I said that I don't sit there with a little bit too much time on my hands and think 'what the hell?' But I'm always pushing, so I've been fighting through it and I'm still fighting through it but I'm much better today than I was in March, April, May, and even into June," confessed Everett.

According to a 2019 analysis written by Columbia University Department of Psychiatry, research suggests that the adult

Black community is 20 percent more likely to experience serious mental health problems, such as Major Depressive Disorder or Generalized Anxiety Disorder. Everett had never really taken a moment to realize how his loss had impacted his mental wellness.

Instead, he decided to manage the uncomfortable emotions by dividing his time between his professional career and his support system. According to a study conducted by Ward, Wiltshire, Detry, and Brown in 2013, Black and African American men are particularly concerned about stigmas surrounding mental health (Ward, Wiltshire, Detry, & Brown, 2013). It was much easier for Everett to deal with his emotional needs by throwing himself into work and spending time with friends.

He knew that the therapy route was not for him, but with the impact of George Floyd's death and having to see the media constantly discussing deaths like those of Kobe Bryant and Chadwick Boseman, Everett was looking for an escape.

To his surprise, being able to reconnect with old college friends like Andrea and others on Zoom was one of his best memories of 2020. They all spent hours catching up with one another and reminiscing on the less stressful days. In the midst of the chaos of 2020, the Zoom gatherings provided Everett with a sense of excitement and relief. Those weekly meetings have continued to give Everett a positive escape to look forward to on every Sunday.

"Connecting with friends, that I would go as far as calling family, has absolutely helped with my mental health," stated a more positive Everett.

It is important to realize and remember that coping can look different for each person. Even though it's not unusual to see people turn to vices like drugs and alcohol to cope, there are healthier techniques available. I'm actively learning which coping skills work best for me. In the past, I've tried distracting myself with work and school. I've even used coloring as a coping mechanism before. But after a few trials and errors, I have found that journaling and listening to music have become my favorite forms of coping.

Nonetheless, the Black experience is not monolith, and neither is our relationship with mental health. With that in mind, I also believe that mental health resources for the Black community are not monolith, therefore neither are our coping mechanisms. Coping can look different for different people. The goal is to find something that works for you, and at least begin to find your support system like Andrea and Everett.

CHAPTER 8

Election Anxiety

—

"It's vindication for a lot of people who have really suffered. You know, that I can't breathe? It wasn't just for George Floyd. It's a lot of people that felt they couldn't breathe…. For a lot of people, today is a good day",

—SAYS AN EMOTIONAL VAN JONES ON CNN AS HE DISCUSSED THE ANNOUNCEMENT OF PRESIDENT ELECT, JOE BIDEN (CNN POLITICS, 2020).

According to the *Oxford English Dictionary's* definition, anxiety is defined as a feeling of worry, nervousness, or unease, typically about an imminent event or something with an uncertain outcome (Oxford Definitions, n.d). So, which events of 2020 comes to mind for you?

I danced with anxiety a few times prior to 2020, but there was no denying its presence during the infamous 2020 Election. This feeling of "election anxiety" was new to me because as a 25-year-old, this was only the second presidential election that I was old enough to participate in. I voted in my very first presidential election in 2016, and in the moment, I didn't feel any real sense of worry or nervousness (at least, not until after the winner was announced). Now, let's flash-forward to the 2020 election. I felt more nervous than ever before the outcome of the election because it seemed as though the fate and wellbeing of the Black community relied upon it.

As far back as 2015, Trump has been connected to documented acts of violence, with perpetrators claiming that he was their inspiration. A 2020 ABC News Report identified at least 54 criminal cases where Trump was invoked in direct connection with violent acts, threats of violence or allegations of assault. Some of these cases include:

Dec. 5, 2015: After Penn State University student Nicholas Tavella, 19, was charged with "ethnic intimidation" and other crimes for threatening to "put a bullet" in a young Indian man on campus, his attorney argued in court that Tavella was just motivated by "a love of country," not by "hate." Tavella's attorney continued to argue in his defense that, "Donald Trump is running for President of the United States saying that, 'We've got to check people out more closely.'" Tavella, who is White, ultimately pleaded guilty to ethnic intimidation and was sentenced to up to two years in prison (Levine, 2020).

Aug. 16, 2016: In Olympia, Washington, 32-year-old Daniel Rowe attacked a White woman and a Black man with a knife after seeing them kiss on a popular street. When police arrived on the scene, Rowe professed to being "a white supremacist" and said "he planned on heading down to the next Donald Trump rally and stomping out more of the Black Lives Matter group." Rowe, who is White, ultimately pleaded guilty to charges of assault and malicious harassment, and he was sentenced to more than 4 years in prison (Levine, 2020).

There is no doubt that having to hear about these acts continued to give anxiety to the minority community. The perpetrators and suspects identified in the 54 cases were mostly white men – as young as teenagers and as old as 75–while the victims largely represented an array of minority groups– African Americans, Latinos, Muslims, and gay men (Levine, 2020). It seemed like as the years of Trump's presidency continued, so did the aggression of these acts on minorities.

By 2020, it seemed that violence had reached an all-time high. In the midst of peaceful protests for George Floyd, there was an enormous amount of violence that continued to center around the Black Lives Matter (BLM) movement.

August 23, 2020: 29-year-old Jacob Blake was shot multiple times in the back by a Kenosha Wisconsin police officer, which left him partially paralyzed. According to a CNN article, Kenosha officers were called to a domestic incident about a woman saying 'her boyfriend was present and was not supposed to be on the premises. When officers arrived, they attempted to arrest Blake and used a taser to try to stop him. Blake then walked around his vehicle, opened the driver's side door, and leaned forward. Police said that about five minutes after the initial report, a dispatcher received reports of shots fired. An officer had grabbed Blake's shirt and fired his service weapon seven times into the 29-year-old's back. (Chavez, 2020).

There was footage of that moment all over the internet and it fueled more protests against police brutality and injustice. A few days later in Kenosha, 17-year-old Kyle Rittenhouse was accused and arrested for shooting three protestors and fatally killing two, with an AR-15 rifle during a BLM demonstration.

Even after video footage circulated on social media of Rittenhouse carrying his rifle and visibly shooting at people, Trump seemingly defending his actions, saying publicly to reporters, "Rittenhouse was trying to get away from them, I guess, it looks like protesters violently attacked him," (Fritz, Johnson &Jackson, 2020).

Even after witnessing white supremacists and other Trump supporters stirring up violence in his honor, Trump never came out publicly to condemn the actions of white supremacy. In fact, when given the chance to denounce white supremacy on the 2020 presidential debate stage against Biden, he said, "Proud Boys, stand back and stand by," (McCammon, 2020).

The fact that Trump could tell the Proud Boys, a known white supremacist group to "stand by," was nerve-wracking to me because I felt that at any moment, he could tell them to attack. And I was nervous and fearful that if he won again, the violence toward minorities would continue to escalate.

ELECTION MONTH

Now, I understand that election year is expected to be filled with constant campaigning and promotion, but election month was a different beast. It tends to be overwhelming and stressful for both politicians and voters. From back-to-back campaign ads, rallies, and debates, both presidential candidates went above and beyond to secure support, even if that meant mentally overloading fellow Americans.

Imagine this. It's November 1st, the beginning of election month and you think you've seen every strategy there is to gain the Black vote. You've seen the emails, answered the daily calls, ignored the random texts, memorized the commercials, swiped past the social media ads, laughed at the memes, watched all the interviews, and even learned the viral TikToks.

Then, you check social media and to your surprise, one of the most influential and well-respected Black rappers in the world, has tweeted and posted picture praising the current President. "Just had a great meeting with @realdonaldtrump @potus besides what he's done so far with criminal reform, the platinum plan is going to give the community real ownership. He listened to what we had to say today and assured he will and can get it done," tweeted the 5x Grammy winner, Lil Wayne (Twitter, 2020).

Spoiler alert. The tweet and photo received mixed reviews from the Black community. Some people were upset at Lil Wayne for supporting someone who has not cared about the Black community. Other people seemed unbothered and indifferent by the photo and Lil Wayne's assumed political stance.

Personally, the 2020 Election seemed more historic than others because the stakes appeared higher for minorities. In a year where many Americans and minority communities alike felt unhappy with the decisions of the current president, a lot was weighing on the outcome of the election. For the Black community in particular, this election was important because of the fact that the current President had spent the last four years creating a more divisive country. Additionally, the outcome of the election could prove to be historic with the potential election of Kamala Harris, the country's first Black female Vice President.

Now, given my experience of isolation over the last few months, I knew "election day anxiety" was inevitable. There had been whispers about potential country-wide riots depending on the winner and even theories that mail-in votes wouldn't be properly counted. Not to mention, both parties were using different strategies to divide and win over Black votes. My emotions were all over the place. I was nervous to vote in person because of COVID-19 concerns, but also anxious to make my voice heard. I was already expecting tension on the actual election day, so I tried to persuade my family to vote early.

The day of early voting, I asked my 19-year-old brother how he felt knowing he was about to vote in his first presidential election. He responded, "It's cool. I feel like I'm doing my part, but I just hope this actually changes something." I didn't tell him at that moment, but I shared the exact same hesitations. Though the lines were long on the first day of early voting in Georgia, it was comforting to witness voters of all ages practice social distancing while waiting to cast their ballot. By the end of early voting, Georgia had displayed an historic turnout. According to the Atlanta Journal Constitution (AJC), by the end of early voting on Friday, nearly 3.9 million Georgians had voted either in-person or by absentee ballot, which amounts to 51 percent of all registered voters (Murphy, 2020).

On election day, Tyler Shaw, a 24-year-old student studying law at Mercer University Law School, decided to spend the day working the polls. She felt the best way to contribute to both the momentous cause and the Black community, would be to assist others and ensure they had a seamless voting experience. By the end of her 8-hour workday with the voting process, she felt she had truly fulfilled her purpose and provided a positive experience to everyone she encountered.

"The highlight of my day was being able to assist a 73-year-old Black man who was voting for the first time ever. He said he couldn't be more excited to participate in this particular election," expressed Shaw.

Even though it seemed that Tyler had found a way to manage her election day anxiety by spending her time working the polls, she was no stranger managing her anxiety in her personal life. At the beginning of 2020, Tyler was starting her second year of law school but was having a difficult time transitioning to virtual learning.

"Look, something has got to give, because I'm not feeling motivated or energized to want to do anything. It's not that I don't care about what I'm doing; it's like I just can't do it. Something is literally debilitating me from doing things," explained Tyler.

At the beginning of the year, she became the Director of Communications for the Southern Region of the Black Law

Students Association, which came with a large amount of responsibility as a Black law student. On a professionally level, she was tasked with communicating Black-related issues from a legal perspective. On a personal level, she was witnessing the how the same legal system treated Black people, in situations like Breonna Taylor's and George Floyd's. So it was safe to say she was drained.

"On top of that, I'm in these spaces [law school] with these people who don't look like me. They have all the privilege. They reek of privilege. And it's like, must be nice to only worry about such small things," she confessed.

After some self-reflection, Tyler still couldn't figure out if those feelings or her lack of motivation was from her study habits, her busy work schedule, or from suddenly having to learn remotely. She decided to go see her doctor.

Her doctor recommended anxiety medication but Tyler, like many people, was hesitant to go the prescription drug route. She felt that with prescription drugs, there is always a chance for addiction to follow. Additionally, some of these medications can come with unfamiliar side effects that can influence the body.

"Well, what are some other options? Because I don't feel like my anxiety is causing these problems. I feel like these problems are causing my anxiety and I don't think medicine is going to magically make me feel better," explained Tyler to her doctor.

Because Tyler was in law school, one of her options included on campus therapy that was covered through her insurance.

So, over the next few weeks, Tyler went and scheduled appointments with two Black psychiatrists who ultimately suggested she begin talk therapy with a new psychologist, who happened to be an older White man.

Tyler has always felt like she can easily open up to practically anyone, so she had no problem talking with her psychologist, despite their apparent differences. What started off as weekly in-person sessions, soon graduated into beneficial virtual sessions.

"In general, [therapy] has made me more reflective. He asked good questions. We have good topics we talk about. We set goals for me to accomplish, and we've made a plan to keep me on track," stated Tyler, as she explained the benefits of therapy.

Her psychologist even helped her come up with the idea to volunteer at the polls to help with the election day anxiety, which proved to be beneficial.

By the end of election night on November 3rd, votes were still being tallied, so it was too early to declare an official winner. By the end of Day 2 of vote counting, the anxiety and fear of the unknown was beginning to kick into overdrive. Millions of Americans were glued to CNN and social media, constantly checking for updates on the race to 270 electoral votes. It actually seemed that the presidential outcome would rely on a few swing states, including Arizona, Nevada, Pennsylvania, and Georgia. All of these states had a national spotlight on them because votes for both candidates were practically split.

This didn't sit right with the current president, who immediately decided to be vocal about the potential of voter fraud. In a briefing statement from the White House, Donald Trump stated:

"Good evening. I'd like to provide the American people with an update on our efforts to protect the integrity of our very important 2020 election. If you count the legal votes, I easily win. If you count the illegal votes, they can try to steal the election from us," (White House Briefing Statements, 2020).

Within the next hour, history had been made again with the state of Georgia voting blue (democratic) for the first time since 1992 (Murphy, 2020). This was historic because Georgia had been known as a reliable Republican state from 1984-2016, with the lone exception of southern democrat, Bill Clinton's presidential election in 1992 (270 To Win- Georgia, 2020). I felt a sense of pride and thrill as I witnessed history being made in my home state.

This prompted the demand for an immediate recount from the Trump White House. However, this win for Joe Biden in Georgia could not be taken away. This was not only a win for many residents in Georgia but was also a win for the large community of Black youth and entrepreneurs that continues to grow.

Despite having factual voting numbers presented during the election, Trump continued to push the voting fraud narrative, and his supporters decided to protest. Nevertheless, on Saturday November 7, by 4 pm loud cheers rang out and honks of cars begin to fill the streets. It had just been announced by CNN that democratic nominee Joe Biden had been projected the winner for the 2020 presidential election (Wagner, 2020). Notably, Biden won the race to 270 with 20 electoral votes from Pennsylvania, beating out his competitor (Wagner, 2020). Moments later, Biden also won electoral votes from Nevada and Arizona, boosting his total to 290 compared to Trump's 214 votes (Wagner, 2020).

Now, it is important to acknowledge that even though Biden won the electoral votes by what some would call a landslide, his margins for the popular votes were significantly slimmer. According to a CNN Politics article published December 2020, Biden had won about 81.2 million votes, and Trump had won about 74.2 million (Sullivan & Agiesta, 2020).

However, that didn't stop states across the country from simultaneously celebrating the results of the presidential election. On the street, Biden and Harris flags were raised with passion by Americans. The media was flooded with scenes of American chanting for the success of Biden and the departure of the current president. At that moment, there seemed to be a sense of relief felt across the country. The past few days had been both mentally and emotional draining for majority of the country. It was freeing to know that change could be on the horizon now.

Joe Biden made his first statement as President-elect saying, "It's time for America to unite and heal," on Twitter.

Vice President elect, Kamala Harris also tweeted "It's about the soul of America and our willingness to fight for it. We have a lot of work ahead of us. Let's get started."

In spite of asking for a recount and simply looking at votes, Trump continued to push the voting fraud narrative and attempted to reassure his supporters by saying "it is fair from over.'"

Nonetheless, this election has been historic for various reasons. According to the Associated Press, Biden, at the age of 78, has become the oldest elected president and oldest president to serve (Barrow, 2021). Kamala Harris has become the first Black and first female vice president ever (Barrow, 2021). According to the *Washington Post*, Trump as became the first president to only serve one term, in the past 30 years (Brockell, 2020). Time Magazine states that the 2020 elections set a record for voter turnout with over 160 million Americans voting in 2020—and voting by mail—than in any other election in US history (Waxman, 2020).

Even though the election wasn't the only time Americans felt anxiety, I am sure a large number of Black Americans would agree that the 2020 election had us anxious, until we heard about the historical win of Biden and Harris.

When you think about the election, did it bring you anxiety at any point? How did Trump's re-election campaign strategy make you feel? Did the constant election tactics ever feel overwhelming? How did you feel when you heard of the Biden/Harris win?

CHAPTER 9

Mental Health Advocates

———

"I learned a long time ago the wisest thing I can do is be on my own side, be an advocate for myself and others like me."
—MAYA ANGELOU.

I consider myself a proud "self-proclaimed" mental health advocate because, to me, an advocate is anyone with a passion to help others. In addition to using this book to share the experiences of others, my advocacy has continued to manifest itself through the launch of my very own mental health awareness and lifestyle brand, Embrace MH LLC. My passion and advocacy have allowed me to use *EmbraceMH Podcast* to amplify the importance of mental health awareness through everyday conversations. I've had conversations with people who have gone through homelessness, small business owners, those who own mental health foundations, and even therapists. All of this encourages others to share their own experiences and find comfort in the stories of others.

Now, according to the National Alliance on Mental Illness (NAMI), "Mental health advocates are heroes—individuals who do not wear capes, but who work tirelessly every day to share their stories and help those who are struggling. They take risks and show their vulnerability by telling their truth in hopes of encouraging someone else."

So, it's safe to say my passion for writing and mental health has classified me as an official mental health advocate… and a hero! Great. That means you can be one too. Who knows? This chapter might prove very useful for you if you share an interest for mental wellness and helping others or have a newfound passion after reading this book.

One of the biggest misconceptions about the title of "mental health advocate" is the idea that you have to have this deep and profound knowledge in all things related to mental health. That's a myth. You really just need to have one simple quality: a passion for the mental health space. Sure, it is good to also be an effective listener or to have some educational background in mental health.

According to NAMI, in addition to sharing your experiences, you can also support someone who needs help, volunteer for a local mental health organization, attend an awareness walk or other event benefiting the mental health movement, encourage your local politicians to prioritize mental health, or simply correct those who use stigmatizing language (Fuller, 2020). And these examples just name a few.

The beauty of mental health advocacy and being an advocate is that if you have the passion for mental health, you can ultimately create your own unique way to contribute to and support the movement.

Like my own journey into advocacy, BJ Armstead, a 24-year-old graduate student at the University of Georgia (UGA) and founder of Apollo Sport Counseling Inc. is using his experience as an athlete and passion for sports to contribute to the mental health space in a very unique way.

I think even BJ would admit his first true love is and probably will forever be the game of baseball. From a very young age, BJ was immersed in every aspect of the baseball world. All throughout middle and high school, he continued to nurture his skills. But subconsciously, another passion was brewing.

BJ's mother has worked as a social worker and counselor since before he was born. So, BJ has lived in an environment that showed him the importance of helping others. Because of this, from a young age he also understood the value of mental health.

"One thing I noticed is the fact that I love athletes, and I felt like, being a former athlete myself, who has gone through stress, anxiety, depression, and trauma—all that stuff—in mental health, but also in athletics, I felt a need to help younger athletes. And to be that person that I wish I had at that age," confessed BJ.

So, after graduating from Morehouse, BJ realized he wanted to continue his family's work and get a Master of Social Work from UGA. We have seen how the media portrays the mental health of many athletes. It seems like they either highlight the negative behaviors caused by mental health or discuss its violent outcomes, like NFL player, Aaron Hernandez's situation. Yet, I rarely hear about the preventative care or programs put in place to address these gaps before it reaches extremes.

Transparent stories from professional athletes about their mental well-being are rarely told. NBA player, Kevin Love, is one of the few professional athletes that has been open about his mental health experience.

> "Five years before the panic attack that everyone knows about, I was probably in the darkest period of my life. I'd only played 18 games with the Timberwolves that season, breaking my right hand twice, and that was when this whole... I guess you'd call it a facade or a character that I had sort of built up... it all started crumbling. I was in a cast. My identity was gone. My emotional outlet was gone. All I was left with was me and my mind. I was living alone at the time, and my social anxiety was so bad that I never even left my apartment. Actually, I would rarely even leave my bedroom. I would have the shades down most of the day, no lights on, no TV, nothing. It felt like I was on a deserted island by myself, and it was always midnight. Just ... dark. Dark and alone with my thoughts. Every. Single. Day." (Love, 2020)

For a lot of athletes, they find themselves under constant pressure and stress from family, coaches, schools, or sponsors, pressuring them to succeed. In addition to that, the majority of sports require them to have excellent physical strength as well. But who teaches them how to mentally handle and adjust to the lifestyle and work ethic of an athlete?

According to a 2020 NCAA Student-Athlete COVID-19 Well-being Survey Report, the rates of mental health concerns experienced within the last month were 150 percent to 250 percent higher than historically reported by NCAA student athletes in the American College Health Association's National College Health Assessment. One can only assume that at some point, even the strongest athletes reach their breaking point. There should be more emphasis on the mental and emotional health of athletes, but for some reason, physical health seems to always take priority.

"Growing up in an area where mental health wasn't really talked about like that, you see a lot of these young men and women and how [mental health] is affecting them, and the effects are generational. That's why I felt the need to really get out there and educate people on things they may not be paying attention to," explained BJ.

Not surprisingly, most members of the Black community are told that their only way "out of the hood" could be through sports, education or the music industry. According to Global Sport Matters, in 2018 the MLB included 7.7 percent African American athletes, the NBA included 80 percent, and 70 percent of the NFL (Tower, 2018). But do any of these athletes have the proper knowledge or tools to deal with the effects of depression, anxiety and trauma professionally and personally?

BJ realized through his own journey through sports and baseball, that when you grow up under the constant pressure of being an athlete, you are only taught how to be an athlete and not how to be a human. When you dedicate and sacrifice your time to being an athlete, you may also be unknowingly sacrificing basic human qualities like self-care and emotion health. Thus, BJ founded Apollo Sports Counseling Inc. He realized that sports had mentally programmed and trained him to not talk and encouraged him to keep many thoughts and feelings buried inside.

There are also other non-profits around like Athletics For Hope, that aims to educate, encourage, and assist athletes in their efforts to engage with community and charitable causes, to increase public awareness of and support for those efforts, and to inspire others to do the same. There are even podcasts available like *I Am Athlete Podcast*, which use the art of conversation to normalize mental wellbeing in athletes.

"So, something I try to impute into my younger athletes now is, I need you to know who you are *outside* of your sport because I learned it was the key to my progress," stated BJ.

As a mental health advocate, one of the best feelings is knowing that you have positively impacted others mental health and life with your actions or support. It has truly been one of the most rewarding titles I've held in life, and I'm not even getting paid to do it. But advocacy can come in many forms and may look different for you. Is mental health advocacy part of your new and adjusted "2020 vision?"

CHAPTER 10

Mental Health Professionals

———

"The scarcity of Black mental health professionals in the US is now an acute problem"

—*DR. ALTHA STEWART, FIRST BLACK PRESIDENT OF AMERICAN PSYCHIATRIC ASSOCIATION.*

I am a firm believer of the idea that "representation actually matters," especially within the mental health profession. It's a hill I am truly committed to dying upon. So, in this chapter, I had the privilege to talk with and better understand the obstacles and experiences of African American mental health professionals and their plans for possible solutions.

Not only did I learn about the various pressures that Black mental health professionals dealt with in 2020, but more personally, this was the closest I had ever been to having my mental health experiences of 2020 validated by Black mental health professionals and experts.

It was refreshing to be able to openly talk about the trauma and anxiety that I felt in 2020 and hear "you're right!" or "I understand and completely agree." It seemed like every emotion that I left over the last year had been validated by the end of our conversation.

"It's been more challenging in a way, because unlike ever before in our history, depending on your age, your [African American psychotherapists] are grappling with the exact same issues, you may be talking about," admitted Charryse Johnson, LCMHC, owner of Jade Integrative Counseling in North Carolina. Johnson is an experienced psychotherapist with fifteen years of specialized work in trauma.

Before my conversation with Charryse, it never crossed my mind to think about how Black mental health professionals navigated the effects of 2020 as it related to their mental health. It is almost ironic, really. I completely forgot that though they are professionally trained to deal with other emotions, they are expected to handle their own. According to the American Psychological Association, African Americans make up 13 percent of the US population. Yet of the estimated 41,000 psychiatrists in the country, only 2 percent are Black (Courtland, 2020). This means, not only are Black mental health professionals underrepresented but they also deal with the constant stress and pressure of being the minority in both a professional and personal capacity.

For Charryse, it was challenging for her to counsel and advise others during the unfolding of the unfortunate Ahmaud Arbery situation. In that situation, before Arbery was shot, the three men charged in his murder engaged in an elaborate chase, hitting the 25-year-old jogger with a truck as he tried to escape them (McLaughlin, 2020).

"That situation rocked me to the core, because at the time I had an 18-year-old son. So, you're sitting there as a mother thinking 'What am I supposed to tell my son? He's right at that age'", explained Charryse.

With those confusing and frustrating thoughts running around her head, Charryse decided the best way to cope with those feelings was to take to social media to vent. It was one of the ways she decided to express her concerns and use her feelings to create awareness. She believes in the benefit of releasing emotions through open and honest communication and not holding them inside. Her coping technique immediately left me more curious about the proper ways to cope, especially with trauma.

The Black community has its fair share of coping methods, which can have both positive and negative effects. After confirming with Charryse, it is safe to say, as a community, our silence and or lack of proper coping skills stems from our history with slavery. When we look at the history of being enslaved, hiding how we felt was protection. For us to stay safe, it was important that we did not show slaveowners outwardly what was going on for us inside. And that is still very much the case. Now, it takes different forms. And again, that's not an one size fits all situation. But historically, that had been the message. For years, it has been seen as a sign of strength among our community. Even though on the inside, things may feel horrible, on the outside, we want people to still think we're okay or fine. And unfortunately, that has become a learned behavior that has been passed down over the generations.

"It's definitely not healthy for us to just move on, but the challenge for many of us is that that's all we know," explained Charryse. "What I'm seeing more from people of color, but specifically in the Black community, is that when we all went into quarantine, it prevented us from avoiding the things that we had stuffed down inside. We told ourselves we were busy and didn't have the time, until we were forced to slow down."

I learned from Charryse that with trauma, it's often "too much, too fast, and too soon". When things happen quickly, there is rarely time to stop or check in with yourself to see what is going on, because you're trying to solve the next thing. We are unfortunately then pushed as a culture into survival mode, and it just becomes "I have to power through, I have to continue to get through until the next thing."

Then, individuals can find themselves carrying those feelings or baggage from one place to the next. So yes, people are attempting to do the best that they can, given the lack of proper resources or knowledge. Granted, it may not be the most ideal thing to do because at some point, what you are running from will catch up to you. No matter how well you think you've done at attempting to suppress the uncomfortable feelings, they always find a way to present themselves. Oftentimes we don't even realize how these feelings are impacting our lives because it's our cycle. It's our pattern. We end up telling ourselves things like 'well, this is who I've always been," which unfortunately only adds to the negative stigma within the community.

"You know, in the Black community, we've always known the magnitude of what we are forced to manage. The challenge is that many of us deal with trauma at such a young age, we're desensitized to it," stated Charryse.

Therapy is a privilege and is not cheap. Many state-run insurance programs don't have proper mental health coverage, so we can still be disadvantaged when it comes to being offered proper access. According to a NAMI article, policies that limit the types of professionals covered under public health programs such as Medicare further compound the barriers to care for these communities. In fact, Medicare specifically excludes licensed professional counselors, as well as marriage and family therapists as covered providers (Toporek & Thakore-Dunlap, 2020). However, Charryse detailed some alternative solutions to therapy which I think could be effective.

"If people aren't open to therapy, doing things like listening circles or brain and body-based approaches such as meditation or yoga can be extremely helpful. Again, everyone has different feelings about these approaches, but I encourage everyone to try at some point in their life," explained a passionate Charryse.

What we don't often realize is we have a habit of self-medicating. We smoke or drink or have casual sex. We oftentimes are just looking to feel something. But all those coping methods are temporary. The only real solution is actively taking the needed steps to work through the trauma.

After speaking with Charryse, I believe that the best way to meet the needs of the community is to lobby for more representation within the field but also to work to train other people in the community to be able to mentally and emotionally support the people around them in some way.

Once again, my theme for a mental health awakening was reconfirmed with Charryse's final statement explaining "what escalated in 2020, I believe was an openness or awareness to a new threshold that a lot of people were up against." I took her "threshold" comment to mean that 2020 made us aware of just how much stress and trauma we can handle before taking the needed steps to act upon it.

After learning more gathering more advice and potential solutions from mental health professionals like Charryse, I decided it was time to explore how larger mental health organizations planned to address and adjust to this mental health awakening in the Black community.

To my surprise, I was able to schedule a conversation with 2021 American Psychological Association (APA) President, Dr. Jennifer Kelly. Dr. Kelly is not only the current APA President, but she also is the former president of the Georgia Psychological Association, and current founding director of Atlanta Center of Behavioral Medicine, where she works with patients with chronic medical conditions as a certified clinical health psychologist.

"2020 has been a challenging year for [mental health] providers in multiple ways. A lot of the nuances you would see in psychotherapy, you don't get to see because of the virtual setting," explained Dr. Jennifer Kelly.

It would be an understatement to say that I was nervous when the call began. I'd never spoken with or interviewed a company president before. But, once again, those nerves were short-lived, as I found myself immediately comforted by her perspective on the impact of 2020.

Within her own personal practice as a clinical health psychologist in Georgia, Dr. Kelly noticed that 2020 impacted both the number of patients she saw and how she interacted with them.

"I have been doing this for a very long time, and I can tell you that there has been a dramatic shift in the direction of improvement in terms of us as a community with mental health. Now since 2020, I have even seen more Black male patients than Black female patients," explained Dr. Kelly.

With her new role as 2021 APA President, Dr. Kelly explained to me that she was more inspired than ever to use her term as president to provide concrete ways in which APA could address health disparities and how the science of psychology best plays a part in advancing health equity. Over the past few years, APA has elected five different African American presidents back-to-back, including current CEO Dr. Arthur Evans.

Because Dr. Kelly is a Black woman herself, it would be difficult for her to ignore the issues that 2020 has highlighted in the Black community. Instead, Dr. Kelly seemed excited to discuss the plans and solutions she had in place as sitting 2021 APA President.

"The pandemic hit, and I thought this was an opportune time for us to address health disparities. So, I put together a task force composed of some of the brightest minds that deal with various areas of health equity, including health in the BIPOC (Black, Indigenous, and other people of color) community, to look at psychological research on public policy, advocacy and systematic racism in health," announced Dr. Kelly.

After our insightful conversation, Dr. Kelly invited me to attend APA's Virtual Town Hall during which she and APA CEO Dr. Arthur Evans would be speaking later that day, and I am extremely glad that I agreed.

Alongside those two experts sat two other APA professionals, who began the discussion with the intended plans and initiatives for APA. Dr. Kelly excitedly talked about the formation and expected progress of the newly appointed Presidential Task Force. They all continued to take turns conversing about the future of psychology as a science and APA as a large, industry-leading organization.

But what piqued my interest the most was hearing about how APA CEO Dr. Arthur Evans responded to a question posed about the future of mental health.

"What is the plausibility of adding a mental health checkup to policy? For instance, at an annual physical or at a semi-annual dental appointment, why not add a mental health checkup?" asked the moderator of the town hall.

Dr. Arthur Evan responded:

"I love the question, because I think it speaks to something that we're really advocating for in APA. And that is true equity between mental and behavioral health care and physical health care. When it comes to physical health care, we talk a lot about prevention. In fact, most cities have a public health department. Actually, all cities have a public health department and in addition to having great hospitals and great primary care, there are a lot of things that we can do to prevent people from being ill.

One of the conceptual shifts that we're trying to make in the way we approach our work is to really talk about those things that are further upstream, that are about prevention, that are about education. They're about psychoeducation and people taking more ownership over their mental health. Particularly, I'm talking broadly about mental health in addition to psychology. We're making that conceptual shift. We talk about it under the rubric of population health, which simply means that in addition to focusing on people once they have a diagnosis, what are the things that we can do for people before they get to that point? The people in the rest of the population are doing a whole population approach where we're looking at prevention, early intervention, psychoeducation, those kinds of things.

What is it that we should be doing to begin the mental health curve that we know is going to happen as a result of the pandemic? We can wait until those people have a diagnosis, or we can do the things that you're suggesting, which is to try to screen patients and identify people early and intervene at that point."

I thought the question was genius, and Dr. Evan's response was even better. Why isn't it yet plausible for us to get mental health checkups policies, similar to dental and physical appointments? Why hasn't universal mental health checkup been posed? Whether this is the sole solution or not, these are the type of questions that should be asked more frequently. How are we actively planning for found solutions to this mental health crisis?

I also completely agreed with Dr. Evan's response to focus on preventative actions that could be taken in order to address the issues before it becomes chronic illnesses. Similar to his recommendation for psychoeducation, I believe it is important to have mental health education and awareness training, especially in minority communities after the events of 2020.

In addition to Dr. Evan's recommendation for psychoeducation and early intervention, another panel member quickly chimed in to mention another potential solution from a fellow APA colleague, Dr. Adrian Williams, who practices out of the University of Illinois Medical School.

"Dr. Williams wrote a paper about a year ago about psychologists being universal mental health primary care providers so that in the same way that primary care physicians provide preventive care, she's proposing psychologists treat patients in a pretty holistic way," stated the panelist.

And in that moment, something clicked for me. I think that Dr. Williams' idea of equipping psychologists to be universal mental health primary care providers to provide preventative care is such a forward-thinking and innovative idea. I truly feel like, not only should psychologists be equipped to act as primary care providers, but members of the community should also be trained to better understand preventative care techniques in the mental health space. I feel that these members should be trained to recognize whether or not an individual should take the next steps to see a professional therapist or psychologist depending on their particular needs.

Whether that first point of preventative contact is a professional therapist, psychologist, teacher, or trained mental health advocate from the community, we as individuals deserve to have our mental health prioritized just like our physical health.

CHAPTER 11

Mental Health Organizations

———

"The experience I have had is that once you start talking about [experiencing a mental health struggle], you realize that actually you're part of quite a big club."

—PRINCE HARRY

In the spirit of learning empathy for others through shared experiences, I immediately bonded with Alison Malmon, the Founder and Executive Director of one the nation's premier mental health nonprofits, Active Minds. I instantly felt comforted in the first moment we connected for our interview.

By the end of our conversation, I felt like we shared more in common than I ever expected. From the outside looking in, most may not expect Alison and I to share similarities, especially seeing that we are opposites in various ways. We are two women of different ages, from different ethnic backgrounds, with different upbringings and different experiences in the world. But the moment I heard her inspiration for creating the nonprofit was because of her older brother, I had an immediate and empathetic connection to her and her experience.

One of my driving forces to advocate for mental health education and awareness within the Black community was wanting to help my own brother process the traumatic and unexpected killing of a close friend.

For the past decade, Alison Malmon and her team have dedicated their time to changing the conversation around mental health among the youth, particularly among high school and college-aged kids.

After experiencing the suicide of her only brother, Brian, Allison founded Active Minds, while she was still a junior at the University of Pennsylvania. Since 2003, Active Minds has been using its platform to impact, engage, and energize young adults. Now, partnering with more than 800 campuses, the organization directly reaches close to 600,000 students each year through campus awareness campaigns, events, advocacy, and outreach (Active Minds, 2020).

"There is a generation right now, who wants to address mental health in a way that is different from how they were raised, and certainly different from how their parents and grandparents' generation was raised," stated Alison, as she explained why Active Minds has been so successful with youth over the years.

"By mobilizing them to share their stories to learn more and give them the words to use, we can and are changing the way America is thinking and talking about mental health."

I fall into the generation that Alison spoke about, and I couldn't agree more. Like Alison, I believe that the youth and younger generations will be the main force in changing the perceptions within the mental health space. The younger generations have realized the importance of addressing mental health different than their parents. I feel that my generation realizes the privilege we have to explore feelings that our parents couldn't or didn't explore. We are witnessing the long-term effects that can ultimately transpire when someone's mental health isn't made priority. We are seeing our parents and elders struggle to communicate effectively and navigate through uncharted feelings from the past. We are seeing how unanswered trauma can still present itself years down the line and we are choosing to take a different route.

Now the youth, being those aged thirty and younger, are on the frontlines, actively working daily to normalizing mental health conversation in our personal and professional worlds. According to the 2020 Deloitte Global Millennial Survey, despite the individual challenges and personal sources of anxiety that millennials and Gen Z are facing, they have remained focused on larger societal issues, both before and after the onset of the pandemic. If anything, the pandemic has reinforced their desire to help drive positive change in their communities and around the world. And they continue to push for a world in which businesses and governments mirror that same commitment to society, putting people ahead of profits, and prioritizing environmental sustainability (Executive Summary, 2020).

"Young adults have identified mental health as their social justice issue," says Alison. "They are going to be the ones that change [how mental health is viewed] for future generations."

Alison has continued to yield effective results by running Active Minds, as not only a nonprofit, but also a mental health marketing organization. Research from a 2018 RAND Corporation impact study confirmed, Active Minds has a significant, positive impact on student health and well-being by creating a supportive climate for mental health on college campuses.

In order to normalize conversations and topics around mental health, Alison noted that when you look at it as a marketing organization, the idea is to take mental health out of the therapist office and look at how mental health impacts everybody every day. By being a marketing organization that talks about mental health in a way that people are experiencing it, Active Minds is continuing to open up everyday conversations, making sure that people know how to recognize certain warning signs in life.

From a marketing standpoint, Active Minds has used its target audience of students, to marketing and share their experiences with each other to create an impact. Through its student ambassador program, student speakers' programs, healthy (school) campus awards, and other initiatives, Active Mind is using the real-life experiences of students to promote the importance of mental health in the youth.

Another highlight of our conversation was when Alison mentioned the impact of "silence" in mental health, which I am very familiar with in the Black community.

"I think silence is the number one impediment to us changing this [stigma] and I also think it is the number one impediment to people being well and feeling better, because it is so hard to break a silence" explained Alison.

Once again, Alison and I were immediately able to relate and empathize on just how detrimental silence has been to the mental health industry. For me, I looked at it from a Black community perspective. There have been various examples throughout the book that illustrate how damaging silence has been in the Black community. As a community, we are no stranger to our silenced and ignored trauma in mental health. However, Alison makes a good point, when she noted to me, "it is a lot easier to elevate a whisper to a speaking voice, but it's hard to break silence."

Her sentiments reconfirmed to me, and hopefully to you as well, how difficult it is for members of the Black community to step out of their comfort zone and begin to discuss and acknowledge certain aspects of their own mental health journey. It is difficult to take those first initial steps. It is hard to begin to find words for unfamiliar feelings and thoughts that have been silenced for years. Breaking the silence is one the most challenging obstacles to address. Compared to our parents who were taught to normalize censorship and silence, we are deciding to be vocal about our feelings and thoughts. Of course, it is not easy to go against societal and community norms. It requires vulnerability. It requires you allowing yourself the grace and a safe space to vocalize thoughts feelings that once had no words.

Also, it was comforting to hear Alison agree that mental health professionals would benefit from understanding the experiences of minorities from a more empathetic lens. She understood that minorities are underrepresented in the mental health space and agreed that empathy is one tool that can be proven to be effective among mental health professionals.

"Not only does everybody need to know how to more appropriately talk to the Black community, minorities, and those experiences that you have, but you deserve to be able to talk to somebody who does know. People of color need to be able to see themselves in the field too, and that's something we've been trying to work on," she stated.

Then, I had the honor of learning more about the Black Mental Health Alliance (BMHA), another non-profit based in Baltimore Maryland, when I was invited to speak on a panel to speak about millennial mental health during the COVID-19 pandemic.

It was such a comforting experience, being able to talk alongside other African American mental health advocates and professionals, to be able to have conversations about millennial mental health in the Black community. During the panel discussion, I learned from Nia Jones, a licensed social worker and youth consultant with the BMHA, that in order to successfully cope with the stresses of 2020, you have to find your personal "mental health cocktail". She explained that coping should a healthy mix of a various coping activities, instead of trying to rely on sole one activity to make you happy.

The unique aspect of BMHA, is that it's dedicated to developing, promoting and sponsoring trusted culturally relevant educational forums and trainings that support the health and well-being of Black people and their communities. As an organization they are constantly providing workshops and forums for the community that connects them with culturally competent and patient-centered, licensed mental health clinicians. You can use these services instead of thinking that therapy is the sole option.

BMHA programming and trainings have primarily focused on historical and race-based trauma, structural racism, cultural competence, mental health stigma, social determinants of health, and mental health in the Black community. Through a use of a membership subscription, you have access to workshops that are specifically catered to the needs and experiences of the Black community.

Additionally, I heard about an emerging behavioral health intervention program developed in Philadelphia by Dr. Riana E. Anderson, assistant professor at the University of Michigan. The Engaging, Managing, and Bonding through Race (EMBRace) program focuses on improving the well-being of Black youth and families by addressing the racial stressors they far too often face. The program does this by combining racial socialization and other racially specific coping strategies with clinically supported stress reduction techniques.

The EMBRace Program is a family program that brings African American or Black identifying youth aged 10-14 and their caregivers together for an hour and a half each week, to engage in conversations about race, cultural pride, discrimination, and stress management. The goal of the EMBRace program is to reduce parent and adolescent racial stress, promote familial bonding, and improve psychological well-being (About Embrace, 2020). And the best part, is families receive compensation for their participation.

It is important to remember that there are other organizations that can also cater to the needs of a broader audience. For instance, Mental Health America (MHA) formally known as the National Mental Health Association, is the nation's leading community-based nonprofit dedicated to promoting mental health through advocacy, education and service. I have used a lot of its online resources, but they also have local affiliates in various states. The National Alliance on Mental Illness (NAMI) is another large organization that not only has great online resources but also has forty-eight state-based organizations that work directly in the community to provide awareness, education and support to those in need. While other organizations like the Anxiety and Depression Association of America (ADAA) are large nonprofits with a more specific focus. The ADAA is concentrated on preventing, treating, and curing anxiety and depression through education and research.

Understanding the benefits that various organization have, I want to encourage everyday citizens to do the needed research to figure out whether the tools offered from mental health organizations will work for them. There are resources available outside of therapy that can provide support. You just have to take the time to seek them out.

CHAPTER 12

Conclusion

———

WHAT IS YOUR NEW "2020 VISION"?

Now that you've had the chance to truly digest the complexity of these topics in their entirety, what does 2020 vision look like for you?

The year 2020 will forever be etched in our American history because of its events and its impact on the country. We all have collectively survived the unexpected complexities of that special year with the needed finesse. Whether we like it or not, the year 2020 will always share a space in our minds and hearts for different reasons. But now, you have read in detail about the intimate struggles of the Black community. You have read about how even though we all have survived an impactful year, that same year, also impacted the mental health of the Black community in a transformative way.

From anxiety, depression, and trauma to isolation and racial discrimination, I hope this book helped open your eyes to the compounding experiences of the African American community in 2020. But I also hope you take time to reflect on how this has affected your perception of the Black community in general. How has that adjusted or added to your 2020 vision? What does 2020 vision look like for you now?

More importantly, let's remember the lessons of 2020. There is a benefit in being able to adjust and adapt your mindset. From a mental health perspective, 2020 awakened us to the benefits of exploring our coping styles and finding our "mental health cocktail." The need for therapy grew. Even through the constant chaos of the year, the mental health industry and its professionals saw a continued demand. We saw people actively seeking out and taking advantage of resources from various mental health organizations. And at the core, we saw the conversation of mental health slowly becoming more normalized.

2020 showed us that "not showing weakness" isn't true strength. Instead, you can find strength in comfort and care. One of the biggest benefits there is for showing empathy to individuals with different backgrounds is the amount of potential similarities that could blossom.

For me, I now live with 2020 vision, which has sparked and awakened me to the potential benefits of mental health education and awareness. But maybe for you, 2020 vision looks a bit different. Maybe you are walking away with a better and more empathetic understanding of the Black experience. Great. Maybe as a professional, you are walking away with a newfound way to better communicate or relate to minorities. Perfect. Maybe, some of these stories have encouraged you to check in on the mental health of a friend or yourself. Regardless of your takeaway, walk away with more knowledge than before on the importance of mental health services in the Black community are important.

How can you do your part to aid in this ongoing conversation and movement?

Remember to PAUSE and be patient with others because you never realize where someone might be within their own mental health journey. Even though it may be tough, try to find the courage to give yourself permission to do things differently.

Acknowledgments

I'd like to acknowledge those who have trusted me enough to share their stories and experiences in the book. Your experiences have helped give this book legs strong enough to move forward:

Miles Williams Jr., Tara Williams, Toni-Ann Hines, Alison Malmon, Dr. Jennifer Kelly, Derrick Johnson, Cletus Emokpae, BJ Armstead, Tyler Shaw, Raymond Stanley, Everett Johnson, Andrea Hazzard, Charryse Johnson LCMHC, Jen Marr

I'd also like to take the time to gratefully acknowledge those that have supported me along this author journey. I truly appreciate all that was done and donated to ensure that this book was published! I would not have been able to make it this far without the support of the following individuals:

Branden Stokes, Nigel Cudjoe, Saqib Qadir, Justin Clay, Calvin Williams, Olivia Greenblatt, Shelia Keys, Bria Maduro, Mary Barner, Tanaya Kollipara, Mia Carmichael, Mary Awoyeye, Devonta Williams, Yolunda Gaines, Tom Spicer, David Moore, Mekeche Camp-Carrell, Christian Ajizian, Melvin Favors,

Linda Atkins, DaVida Roberts, Jimmy Williams, Cassandra Graham, Kristie Moore, Preston Carter, Nathan Aferi, Craig Lewis, Jefrie liburd, Qiana Bennett, Derhyl Middleton, Jonathan Phillips, Carol Cook, Lynn Martin, Fe'Dricka Moore, James Blount, Jimela Hankins Ellis, Audrey Callender, Dr.Charles Best, Charlette Goggins, Traci Browne, Sharon Armstrong, Abby Pepper, Black Mental Health Alliance, Michelle Hall, Priscilla Segnini, Jasmin Jeffries, Makeeda Collins, Cynthia Tucker, Jill Bornstein, Stephanie Keeling, Lytanda Zellner, Brianna Figueroa, Kenyanee Releford, Audra Madison, Jonathon Daniell, Seth Clarke, Jessica Stewart, Kendra Stewart, Christopher Williams, Jocelayna Howard, Melissa Lopez, Subrena Robinson, Nancy Glover, Gail Ransome, Stacy Fredericks, Yuvonne Grant, Elizabeth Beresford, Eric Koester, Daria Fish, Deserae Lane, Leslie Galbreath, Oceane Tanny

Appendix

———

Introduction

"2021 Covid-19 and Mental Health: A Growing Crisis." Mental Health America. Accessed November 2020. https://mhanational.org/sites/default/files/Spotlight%202021%20-%20COVID-19%20and%20Mental%20Health.pdf.

"Basic Facts About Depression." Mental Health America. Accessed November 2020. https://www.mhanational.org/conditions/depression.

"Depression in Black America." Mental Health America. Accessed November 2020 https://www.mhanational.org/depression-black-americans.

"Facts and Statistics." Anxiety and Depression Association of America. Accessed November 2020. https://adaa.org/about-adaa/press-room/facts-statistics.

McGuire, Thomas, and Jeanne Miranda. "Racial and Ethnic Disparities in Mental Health Care: Evidence and Policy Implications." February 18, 2018. https://www.ncbi.nlm.nih.gov/pmc/articles/PMC3928067/.

"Stress In America 2020: A National Mental Health Crisis." American Psychology Association. Accessed November 2020. https://www.apa.org/news/press/releases/stress/2020/sia-mental-health-crisis.pdf.

Terlizzi, EP, and B. Zablotsky. "Mental Health Treatment Among Adults: United States, 2019." NCHS Data Brief, no 380. Hyattsville, MD: National Center for Health Statistics. (2020). https://www.cdc.gov/nchs/products/databriefs/db380.htm.

Vance, Thomas, Phd. "Addressing Mental Health in the Black Community." February 8, 2019. https://www.columbiapsychiatry.org/news/addressing-mental-health-black-community.

CHAPTER 1

Davis, Tchiki PhD. "Sympathy vs. Empathy: How Does Sympathy Differ from Empathy? And What About Compassion?" July 14, 2020. https://www.psychologytoday.com/us/blog/click-here-happiness/202007/sympathy-vs-empathy.

Inspiring Comfort. "Empathy-Action Gap." Accessed May 2021. https://www.inspiringcomfort.com/.

Merriam-Webster Dictionary. "Definition of Empathy." Accessed November 2020. https://www.merriam-webster.com/dictionary/empathy.

Marriam-Webster Dictionary. "Definition of Comfort." Accessed November 2020 https://www.merriam-webster.com/dictionary/comfort.

Riess, Helen MD. "The Science of Empathy." May 9, 2017. https://www.ncbi.nlm.nih.gov/pmc/articles/PMC5513638/#:~:text=Empathy%20is%20a%20Hardwired%20Capacity&text=Patients%20unconsciously%20mimic%20the%20actions,the%20person%20they%20are%20observing_.

CHAPTER 2

Cohen, Li. "Police in the U.S. Killed 164 Black People in the First 8 Months of 2020. These Are Their Names. (Part I: January-April)." September 10, 2020. https://www.cbsnews.com/pictures/black-people-killed-by-police-in-the-u-s-in-2020/_.

COVID Data Tracker. "United States COVID-19 Cases, Deaths, and Laboratory Testing (RT-PCR) by State, Territory, and Jurisdiction." Accessed on November 2020. _https://covid.cdc.gov/covid-data-tracker/#cases_casesper100klast7days_.

Doha Madani. "America's Racial Reckoning is Putting a Spotlight on Black Mental Health." September 26, 2020. https://www.nbcnews.com/news/nbcblk/america-s-racial-reckoning-putting-spotlight-black-mental-health-n1241127_.

Gould, Elise, and Valerie Wilson. "Black Workers Face Two of the Most Lethal Preexisting Conditions for Coronavirus—Racism and Economic Inequality." June 1, 2020. https://www.epi.org/publication/black-workers-covid/_.

Hartman, Travis, S. Hart, J. Marte, and H. Scheider. "The Race Gap: Black White." Accessed on June 2021. https://graphics. reuters.com/GLOBAL-RACE/USA/nmopajawjva/#0.

Laurencin, Cato T., and Joanne M. Walker. "A Pandemic on a Pandemic: Racism and Covid-19 in Blacks." July 11, 2020. _https://www.ncbi.nlm.nih.gov/pmc/articles/PMC7375320/_.

"Mapping Police Violence." Updated as of May 2021. _https://mappingpoliceviolence.org/_.

Statista Research Department. "Unemployment Rate in the United States in 2020, by Ethnicity." March 9, 2021. https://www.statista.com/statistics/237917/us-unemployment-rate-by-race-and-ethnicity/.

Vanderbeek, Thomas. "Disparities in PPP Lending by Race." March 18, 2021. https://theinstitutenc.org/2021/03/disparities-in-ppp-lending-by-race/.

Washington Post. "945 People Have Been Shot and Killed By Police in the Past Year." Accessed on November 2020. https://www.washingtonpost.com/graphics/investigations/police-shootings-database/_.

CHAPTER 3

Anneken, Tappe. "30 Million Americans Have Filed Initial Unemployment Claims Since Mid-March." April 30, 2020. www.cnn.com/2020/04/30/economy/unemployment-benefits-coronavirus/index.html_.

Humble the Poet. *Unlearn: 101 Simple Truths for a Better Life.* New York: HarperCollins Publishers, 2019.

Humble the Poet. *Unlearn: 101 Simple Truths for a Better Life.* New York: HarperCollins Publishers, 2019.

Mental Health America. "Black And African American Communities and Mental Health." Accessed on November 2020. _https://www.mhanational.org/issues/black-and-african-american-communities-and-mental-health_.

Mental Health America. "The State of Mental Health in America." Accessed on December 2020. https://www.mhanational.org/issues/state-mental-health-america_.

CHAPTER 4

"Coping with Racial Trauma." University of Georgia Department of Psychology. Accessed on June 2021. https://www.psychology.uga.edu/coping-racial-trauma.

Darling-Hammond, Linda. "Unequal Opportunity: Race and Education." March 1, 1998. https://www.brookings.edu/articles/unequal-opportunity-race-and-education/.

Emma Goldberg. "What It's Like to be a Teacher in 2020 America." October 28, 2020. https://www.nytimes.com/2020/10/05/us/teachers-covid-schools-pandemic.html.

Geiger, A.G. "America's Public School Teachers Are Far Less Racially and Ethnically Diverse Than Their Students." August 27, 2018. https://www.pewresearch.org/fact-tank/2018/08/27/

americas-public-school-teachers-are-far-less-racially-and-eth-
nically-diverse-than-their-students/.

Myers, Justus, and Phillip A. Wallach. "The Federal Government's
Coronavirus Response—Public Health Timeline." Brookings
Institute. March 31, 2020. https://www.brookings.edu/research/
the-federal-governments-coronavirus-actions and fail-
ures-timeline-and-themes/.

NCES: Digest of Educational Statistics. "Estimated Average
Annual Salary of Teachers in Public Elementary and Secondary Schools, by State: Selected Years, 1969-70 through 2016-17."
Accessed on December 2020. https://nces.ed.gov/programs/
digest/d17/tables/dt17_211.60.asp.

National School Boards Association. "Black Students in the Condition of Education 2020." June 23, 2020. https://www.nsba.
org/Perspectives/2020/black-students-condition-education.

Walker, Tim. "Where Do Teachers Get the Most Respect?" November 11, 2018. https://www.nea.org/advocating-for-change/new-
from-nea/where-do-teachers-get-most-respect.

CHAPTER 5

Carlisle, Madeleine. "Two Black Trans Women Were Killed in the
U.S. in the Past Week as Trump Revokes Discrimination Protections for Trans People." *Time*. June 13, 2020. https://time.
com/5853325/black-trans-women-killed-riah-milton-domi-
nique-remmie-fells-trump/.

Earl, T. R., M. Alegría, F. Mendieta, and Y. D. Linhart. "Just Be Straight with Me: An Exploration of Black Patient Experiences in Initial Mental Health Encounters." *The American Journal of Orthopsychiatry.* 81(4), 519–525. (2011). https://www.ncbi.nlm. nih.gov/pmc/articles/PMC3220950/.

Elliott Kozuch. "HRC Mourns Merci Mack, Black Trans Woman Killed in Dallas." Human Rights Campaign. July 2, 2020. https://www.hrc.org/news/hrc-mourns-merci-mack-black-transgender-woman-killed-in-dallas.

Elliot Kozuch. "HRC Mourns Nina Pop, Black Trans Woman Killed in Missouri." Human Rights Campaign. May 5, 2020. https://www.hrc.org/news/hrc-mourns-nina-pop-black-transgender-woman-killed-in-missouri.

Jones, Imara. Instagram. Accessed on November 2020. https://www.instagram.com/imara_jones_/.

Jones, Imara. "Iyanna Dior's Beating Proves Black Lives Still Don't Matter If You're Trans." *The Grio,* June 4, 2020. https://thegrio.com/2020/06/04/iyanna-dior-black-lives-matter/.

Mental Health America. "Racism And Mental Health." Accessed on June 2021. https://www.mhanational.org/racism-and-mental-health.

"People with Moderate to Severe Asthma." Centers for Diseases Control and Prevention. Last Updated September 11, 2020. https://www.cdc.gov/coronavirus/2019-ncov/need-extra-precautions/asthma.html.

Ricardo, Alonso-Zaldivar. "Trump Administration Revokes Transgender Health Protection." *Associated Press News*, June 12, 2020. https://apnews.com/article/bae1456be55955aab379a3541391f93b.

CHAPTER 6

Centers for Disease Control and Prevention "Leading Causes of Death - Males - Non-Hispanic Black - United States." Minority Health and Health Equity. (2016). _/healthequity/lcod/men/2016/nonhispanic-black/index.htm#anchor_1571149616_.

Giffords Law Center to Prevent Gun Violence. "Statistics." Accessed November 2020. _https://giffords.org/lawcenter/gun-violence-statistics/_.

Kennard, Jerry. "Health Statistics for Black American Men." April 16, 2020. https://www.verywellhealth.com/black-american-mens-health-2328772.

Koch, Christof. "What Near-Death Experiences Reveal about the Brain." June 1, 2020. https://www.scientificamerican.com/article/what-near-death-experiences-reveal-about-the-brain/.

Lin, Luona, MPP, Karen Stamm, PhD, and Peggy Christidis, PhD. "How Diverse is the Psychology Workforce?" American Psychological Association Datapoint Center. (2018). _https://www.apa.org/monitor/2018/02/datapoint_.

Motley, Robert, and Andrae Banks. "Black Males, Trauma, and Mental Health Service Use: A Systematic Review." (2018). https://www.ncbi.nlm.nih.gov/pmc/articles/PMC6292675/_.

Neighbors, Harold "Woody" PhD. "Manning Up" Can Often Bring Men Down." Association of American Medical Colleges. (2019). https://www.aamc.org/news-insights/manning-can-often-bring-men-down_.

Smith, Jocelyn R. PhD. LGMFT. "Unequal Burdens of Loss: Examining the Frequency and Timing of Homicide Deaths Experienced by Young Black Men Across the Life Course." (2015). doi: 10.2105/AJPH.2014.302535 https://www.ncbi.nlm.nih.gov/pmc/articles/PMC4455517/_.

CHAPTER 7

Arizton Advisory & Intelligence. "The Telehealth Market in US to Reach Revenues of Over $25 Billion During the Period 2020 –2025." Market Research by Arizton. Cision PR Newswire. April 15, 2020. https://www.prnewswire.com/news-releases/the-telehealth-market-in-us-to-reach-revenues-of-over-25-billion-during-the-period-2020-2025---market-research-by-arizton-301040962.html.

Nodell, Bobbi. "Study: Pandemic Halts, Delays 28 Million Elective Surgeries." May 19, 2020. https://newsroom.uw.edu/postscript/study-pandemic-halts-delays-28-million-elective-surgeries.

Tyring, Ariel MD, Steven S. Saraf, MD, and Lisa C. Olmos de Koo, MD. "Top Five Pointers for Working with Silicone Oil." *Retina Today.* August 2018. https://retinatoday.com/articles/2018-july-aug/top-five-pointers-for-working-with-silicone-oil.

Vance, Thomas A. Ph.D. "Addressing Mental Health in the Black Community." Columbia University Department of Psychiatry.

February 9, 2019. https://www.columbiapsychiatry.org/news/addressing-mental-health-black-community.

Ward, Earlise C, Jacqueline C. Wiltshire, Michelle A. Detry, and Roger L. Brown. "African American Men and Women's Attitude Toward Mental Illness, Perceptions of Stigma, and Preferred Coping Behaviors." *Nursing Research.* (2013). ⋗, 62 ⋗(3), 185-194. https://doi:10.1097/NNR.0b013e31827bf533.

"Why Getting Medically Misdiagnosed Is More Common Than You May Think." *Healthline.* Accessed on Jan 2021. https://www.healthline.com/health-news/many-people-experience-getting-misdiagnosed#Medical-misdiagnoses-are-more-common-than-most-people-realize.

CHAPTER 8:

"270 To Win- Georgia." Accessed June 2021. https://www.270towin.com/states/Georgia.

Barrow, Bill. "At 78 and the Oldest President, Biden Sees a World Changed." *AP News.* January 23, 2021. https://apnews.com/article/biden-inauguration-joe-biden-race-and-ethnicity-ronald-reagan-pennsylvania-48d1659d4469999be87fbd-87d560a52c.

Brockell, Gillian. "Trump Just Joined History's Club of One-Term Presidents, Rejected by the Americans They Led." *Washington Post.* November 7, 2020. https://www.washingtonpost.com/history/2020/11/07/one-term-presidents-trump/.

Chavez, Nicole. "What We Know So Far About Jacob Blake's Shooting." *CNN*. August 27, 2020. https://www.cnn.com/2020/08/27/us/jacob-blake-shooting-what-we-know/index.html.

CNN Politics. "Van Jones: For a Lot of People It's a Good Day." November 2020. https://www.cnn.com/videos/politics/2020/11/07/van-jones-reaction-2020-election-result-election-night-vpx.cnn.

"Definitions Anxiety." Oxford Definitions Online. Accessed on November 2020. https://www.lexico.com/en/definition/anxiety.

Levine, Mike. "'No Blame?' ABC News Finds 54 Cases Invoking 'Trump' in Connection with Violence, Threats, Alleged Assaults." *ABC News*. May 30, 2020. https://abcnews.go.com/Politics/blame-abc-news-finds-17-cases-invoking-trump/story?id=58912889.

Lil Wayne Weezy F. Twitter. October 29, 2020. https://twitter.com/LilTunechi/status/1321941986174226432.

McCammmon, Sarah. "From Debate Stage, Trump Declines To Denounce White Supremacy." *NPR*. September 30, 2020. https://www.npr.org/2020/09/30/918483794/from-debate-stage-trump-declines-to-denounce-white-supremacy.

Murphy, Patrica. "Stacey Abrams' Georgia Turning Blue." *Atlanta Journal Constitution*, November 6, 2020. https://www.ajc.com/politics/politics-blog/stacey-abrams-georgia-turning-blue/CN4QYWABYZDLDOBKVY5TMQMT5I/.

Sullivan, Kate, and Jennifer, Agiesta. "Biden's Popular Vote Margin Over Trump Tops 7 Million." *CNN*. December 4, 2020. https://www.cnn.com/2020/12/04/politics/biden-popular-vote-margin-7-million/index.html.

Substance Abuse and Mental Health Services Administration: "The Opioid Crisis and the Black/African American Population: an Urgent Issue." Publication No. PEP20-05-02-001. Office of Behavioral Health Equity. Substance Abuse and Mental Health Services Administration. (2020). https://store.samhsa.gov/sites/default/files/SAMHSA_Digital_Download/PEP20-05-02-001_508%20Final.pdf.

Wagner, Meg, Fernando Alfonso III, M. Macay, M. Mahtani, V. Rocha, and A. Wills. "Joe Biden Election President." *CNN*. November 8, 2020. https://www.cnn.com/politics/live-news/trump-biden-election-results-11-07-20/index.html.

Waxman, Olivia. "The 2020 Election Set a Record for Voter Turnout. But Why Is It Normal for So Many Americans to Sit Out Elections?" *Time*. November 5, 2020. https://time.com/5907062/record-turnout-history/.

White House Briefing. "President Trump Statements." November 2020. https://www.whitehouse.gov/briefings-statements/remarks-president-trump-election/.

CHAPTER 9

Fuller, Kristen. "What Does It Mean to be a Mental Health Advocate." National Alliance on Mental Health. June 24, 2020.

https://www.nami.org/Blogs/NAMI-Blog/June-2020/What-Does-It-Mean-to-Be-a-Mental-Health-Advocate_.

Love, Kevin. "To Anybody Going Through It." *The Players' Tribune*. September 17, 2020. https://www.theplayerstribune.com/articles/kevin-love-mental-health.

NCAA Student-Athlete COVID-19 Well-being Survey. "Mental Health Concerns." (2020). https://ncaaorg.s3.amazonaws.com/research/other/2020/2020RES_NCAASACOVID-19Survey-Report.pdf.

Tower, Nikole. "In an Ethnic Breakdown of Sports, NBA Takes Lead For Most Diverse." *Global Sport Matters*. December 18, 2018. https://globalsportmatters.com/culture/2018/12/12/in-an-ethnic-breakdown-of-sports-nba-takes-lead-for-most-diverse/_.

CHAPTER 10

McLaughlin, Elliott. "Ahmaud Arbery Was Hit with a Truck Before He Died, and His Killer Allegedly Used a Racial Slur, Investigator Testifies." *CNN*. June 4, 2020. https://www.cnn.com/2020/06/04/us/mcmichaels-hearing-ahmaud-arbery/index.html.

Milloy, Courtland. "Black Psychiatrists Are Few. They Have Never Been More Needed." *Washington Post*, August 11, 2020. https://www.washingtonpost.com/local/black-psychiatrists-are-few-theyve-never-been-more-needed/2020/08/11/7df9eeea-dbeb-11ea-8051-d5f887d73381_story.html_.

Toporek, Rebecca Ph.D., and Ulash Thakore-Dunlap, LMFT. "How the Pandemic Has Magnified Mental Health Care Disparities." National Alliance of Mental Illness. July 29, 2020. https://www.nami.org/Blogs/NAMI-Blog/July-2020/How-the-Pandemic-Has-Magnified-Mental-Health-Care-Disparities.

CHAPTER 11

Active Minds. "Landmark Study Confirms Active Minds Has a Significant Impact on Student Mental Health and Well-Being." Accessed on June 2021. https://www.activeminds.org/about-us/mission-and-impact/study/.

Active Minds. "Our Story." Accessed on November 2020. https://www.activeminds.org/about-us/our-story/.

Deloitte Global Millennial Survey 2020: Executive Summary. "Millennials and Gen Zs hold the key to creating a 'better normal'." (2020). *Deloitte.* https://www2.deloitte.com/global/en/pages/about-deloitte/articles/millennialsurvey.html.

Deloitte News Release. "Deloitte Survey Reveals 'Resilient Generation': Millennials and Gen Zs Hard Hit by COVID-19 Pandemic, Yet View This Period as an Opportunity to Reset, Take Action." June 25, 2020. *Deloitte.* https://www2.deloitte.com/global/en/pages/about-deloitte/press-releases/deloitte-millennial-survey-reveals-resilient-generation.html.

The Embrace Program. "About Embrace." Accessed June 2021. https://www.theembraceprogram.com/about.